RADIAL

PARALLEL

AS SEEN BY EYE

AS SEEN ORTHOGRAPHICALLY

RADIAL

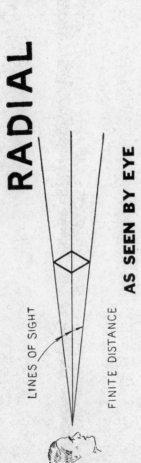

LINES OF SIGHT

FINITE DISTANCE

AS SEEN BY EYE

PARALLEL

LINES OF SIGHT

INFINITE DISTANCE

AS SEEN ORTHOGRAPHICALLY

AUDELS ANSWERS
ON
BLUE PRINT READING

FOR MECHANICS AND BUILDERS

BY F.D. GRAHAM

THEO. AUDEL & CO., PUBLISHERS
49 WEST 23RD ST. NEW YORK.

Reprinted 1953

LIST OF CHAPTERS

Author's Note

A blue print or working drawing may be considered as virtually a mirror which not only *reflects* but *fixes* on paper the ideas of the draughtsman-designer which he wishes to convey to the mechanic in the shop or on the job.

Working drawings are based on *orthographic projection* in which only a few lines are required to picture an object; thus it may be called a kind of *graphic short hand*.

The purpose of the author is to present the key to orthographic projection in so simple a manner that it can be easily and quickly understood.

The various notations, abbreviations, terms, etc., as found on some blue prints are given in separate chapters, explaining architects, ship fitters, air craft and other classes of blue prints.

An expression of appreciation is here given:

To E. W. Lawson for efficient secretarial work, including proof reading and checking.

To Geo. W. Hood for skillful execution of line drawings from the author's pencil sketches.

To J. J. O'Riordan for efficient type setting, collating and make up, and William C. McCracken for efficient monotype composition.

To the publishers for suggesting that I write this book.

FRANK D. GRAHAM.

INDEX

For Quick Reference in Answering Your Question or Problem.

A

F

G

H

I

L

M

N

O

U

V

T

W

Z

W

T

CHAPTER 1

Blue Prints

Ques. What is a blue print?

Ans. A print of a drawing in which the lines are white on a blue background.

Ques. How is the term blue print incorrectly applied?

Ans. When applied to other process prints such as brown prints, or blue line prints.

Since working drawings are usually printed blue prints the term blue print is loosely used regardless of the printing process.

Ques. How is a blue print made?

Ans. From a *tracing*, similar to making a photographic print.

That is, the tracing is placed over a framed glass plate and over this a sensitized sheet of paper. The assembly is then tightly pressed against the glass by pressure of a spring clamp exerted on the back.

When exposed to light the paper turns a pale green color except in places covered by lines of the drawing which exclude the light. When sufficiently exposed the paper is immersed in water and the portion of the paper acted upon by the light turns blue.

Fig. 1 shows a solar printing frame and fig. 2 an electric outfit.

Ques. What is a tracing?

Ans. A copy in ink of the original pencil drawing made on either tracing paper or preferably tracing cloth.

Ques. What is the advantage of a tracing?

Ans. As many blue prints can be made from the tracing as desired.

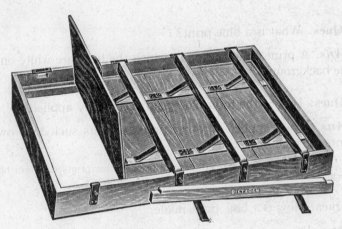

Fig. 1.—Dietzgen solar printing frame.

It becomes a permanent record of the drawing and is filed in suitable drawers for use any time additional prints are wanted.

Ques. What is the objection to tracing paper?

Ans. Although cheaper than tracing cloth it is easily torn.

Ques. How long does it take to make a blue print?

Ans. About the same time as a photographic print (a few minutes) depending upon the type paper used.

Dietzgen for instance classify their blue print papers as: slow, rapid, extra rapid, electric rapid, and double electric. These papers require exposures ranging from about four minutes to ten to twenty seconds in bright sunlight.

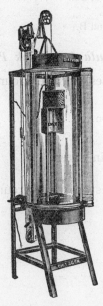

FIG. 2.—Dietzgen vertical electric printing machine and sheet washer. *The machine consists of* a half cylinder of glass having an open printing surface of 24 ×36 ins. This glass is held in a felt-lined metal frame. The tracing and sensitized papers are held in place by roller curtains. The arc lamp consumes 15 amperes on 110 or 220 volts, direct or alternating current. It is provided with a satin-finished aluminum reflector of such shape as to give the best possible distribution of light. A pneumatic speed regulator is provided which insures uniform speed in the descent of the arc lamp. The light is automatically extinguished at any desired point by means of a tripping device. This device permits the machine to be loaded, set in operation and left unattended, without any possibility of the print becoming over-exposed through the continued burning of the light.

Formulae for Print Solutions.—For those who desire to make their own prints the following solutions are recommended:

Formula for Blue Print Solution.

Dissolve thoroughly and filter

A. Red prussiate of potash............................ 2½ ounces
Water.. 1 pint
B. Ammonium-citrate of iron........................ 4 ounces
Water.. 1 pint
Use equal parts of A and B.

Formula far Black Prints

Negatives. White lines on blue ground; prepare the paper with:

Ammonia-citrate of iron.............................. 40 grains
Water... 1 ounce

After printing wash in water.

Positives. Black lines on white ground; prepare the paper with:

Iron perchloride....................................... 616 grains
Oxalic acid.. 308 grains
Water.. 14 ounces

Develop in:

Gallic acid... 1 ounce
Citric acid... 1 ounce
Alum... 8 ounces

Use 1¼ ounces of developer to 1 gallon of water. Paper is fully exposed when it has changed from yellow to white.

Ques. What is the objection to sunlight exposure in making blue prints?

Ans. Its uncertainty.

This is avoided by the use of electric machines with automatic light control.

Ques. What is a Van Dyke print?

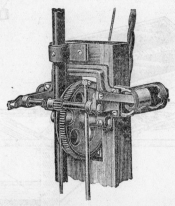

FIG. 3.—Dietzgen speed regulator for vertical electric printing machine. By turning a rod, which governs the regulations, any desired speed in the descent of the lamp can be obtained. The electric current is automatically cut off and the light extinguished at any desired point by means of a tripping device.

Ans. A process giving white lines on a dark brown background.

The brown coating being impervious to the rays of light makes it possible to print with a Van Dyke the same as with a tracing.

Ques. What results are obtained by using a Van Dyke with blue print paper?

Ans. A print having blue lines on white background.

Blue Print Reading.—The question is often asked, "Is it necessary to become a mechanical draughtsman to learn blue print reading." The answer is "No."

However, in the study of mechanical drawing the student learns may things necessary in reading blue prints. For instance, the significance in the different lines used and various other conventions applied to making drawings.

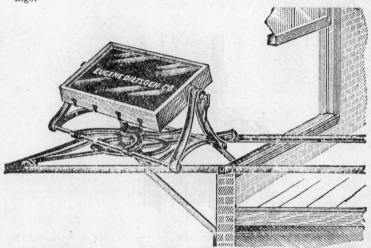

Fig. 4.—Turntable carriage. A convenient means of exposing prints outside of the window. The carriage is mounted on an iron turntable which is on four wheels. The frame which revolves between the standards of the carriage can be rolled outside of the window and turned to face the direct rays of the sun.

Ques. What is the advantage of knowing how to read blue prints?

Ans. The mechanic does not have to frequently ask the foreman to explain parts of the drawing.

Ques. What does a blue print show?

Ans. A *working drawing* of an object.

Ques. What happens if some of the dimensions be omitted on the blue print?

Ans. An attempt by the mechanic to scale them off the blue print usually results in errors.

Ques. Why?

Ans. Because of shrinkage and creases in the paper.

FIG. 5.—Dietzgen junior blue print washer.

Ques. What should be done in such cases?

Ans. The print should be returned to the draughting room so that the missing dimension or dimensions may be obtained by scaling the original pencil drawing.

Ques. What precaution should be taken in scaling the original pencil drawing?

Ans. One or two of the dimensions should be tested for shrinkage of the pencil drawing.

Ques. What is a working drawing?

Ans. One or more drawings completely showing the outlines of an object to scale, with all dimensions and other data necessary for the mechanic to make the object *without asking questions*.

The number of drawings or "views" necessary to completely show the object is determined by the draughtsman.

Ques. How is it possible to fully show on a blue print the actual shape of an object of complicated contour?

Ans. By a system of representations known as orthographic projection.

As this is the system used, thorough knowledge of this system is necessary in order to read a blue print. This is explained at length in a later chapter and there should be no difficulty in understanding its basic principles if the text be well studied.

CHAPTER 2

The Scale

Ques. What is the first thing a draughtsman should do before making a drawing?

Ans. He should mark with heavy pencil in large letters the *scale* of the drawing.

Ques. Why so prominently?

Ans. So it won't take all night to find it.*

Ques. What is the scale?

Ans. As applied to a drawing it is a ratio which indicates the relation between the size of the drawing and the size of the object drawn.

Ques. How is the scale usually expressed on a drawing?

Ans. As full size, half size, quarter size, etc.

*NOTE.—Excuse the exaggeration, but that's the only way to knock it into some people's heads.

The Scale.—Evidently on a full size drawing the object and drawing are of the same size. When the drawing is marked half size, the object is twice the size of the drawing.

Thus in figs. 1 to 4, drawings of an object are shown full size, half size and quarter size. That is to say, if the object be a cylindrical piece whose height (full size in fig. 1) is represented by **H** and diameter by **D,** then for the full size drawing fig. 2, these dimensions will be the same. That is, $H = h$; $D = d$.

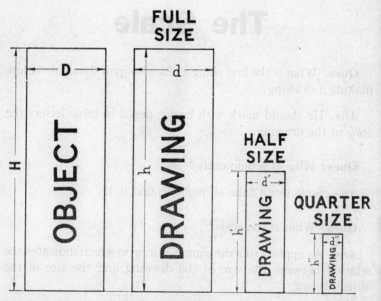

FIGS. 1 to 4.—**Drawing of an object** to *different scales* as: full size, half size, quarter size. Note difference in the length of the dimensions (H, D; h, d, $h'd'$ and $h''d''$) for the different scales.

Now for the half size drawing, fig. 3, $h' = \frac{1}{2}H$; $d' = \frac{1}{2}D$. Similarly for the quarter size drawing fig. 4 $h'' = \frac{1}{4}H$; $d'' = \frac{1}{4}D$.

From this it is seen (in figs. 1 and 2) that when the length of any edge on the drawing is made the same as the length of the corresponding edge on the object the drawing is marked *full size*, sometimes *actual size*. Similarly (in figs. 1 and 3) if the length of any line on the drawing be half the length of the corresponding line on the object, the drawing is *half size*.

Ques. What are the reasons for making drawings of large objects to half or quarter scale?

Ans. For convenience in handling, reduction of time in draughting and to render them more easily read.

Ques. Give another reason for using different scales.

Ans. To make possible the use of sheets all of the same size to fit in the drawers of the filing system in use.

Evidently to draw objects of different size on same size sheets, different scales must be used so that the drawing won't "run off the paper."

Ques. Give another method of expressing the scale of a drawing.

Ans. The ratio of the two sizes may be expressed as 1 : 4 or simply fractional as $\frac{1}{4}$.

Here 1 : 4 or $\frac{1}{4}$ is the same as "quarter size."

Ques. How do architects usually express the scale?

Ans. Arithmetically as for instance $1'' = 1'$.

Ques. What does this mean?

Ans. It indicates that 1 inch on the drawing is equal to one foot on the object.

Ques. Give an objectionable way of stating $1'' = 1'$.

Ans. 1" to the foot.*

Ques. What kind of draughtsman's scales are used in drawing small objects?

Ans. Flat or triangular draughtsman's scales, with dimensions such as: ⅛, ¼, ⅜, ½, ¾ and 1 inch to the inch. See fig. 6.

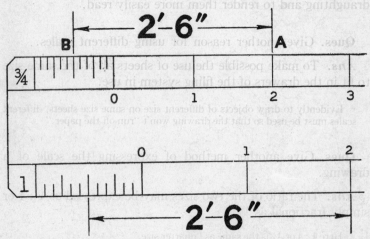

FIG. 5.—Typical draughtsman *architects' scales* detail showing ¾ and 1 in. to the foot and how to take measurements.

Ques. Describe the architect's scales.

Ans. They are made flat or triangular. The end inch is divided into twelve equal parts.

---

*NOTE.—Some mathematical highbrows are so highbrow that it pains them to see an expression like $1'' = 1'$ although they know perfectly well that it is an abbreviation for "1" on the drawing is equal to 1' on the object."

Triangular six scale architect's scales provide for various size drawings so that—

$$1 \text{ inch on scale} = 1 \text{ foot}$$

$$\tfrac{3}{4} \text{ inch on scale} = 1 \text{ foot}$$

$$\tfrac{1}{2} \text{ inch on scale} = 1 \text{ foot}$$

etc.

Fig. 5 shows detail of architect's flat scale with ¾ and 1 inch to the foot scales.

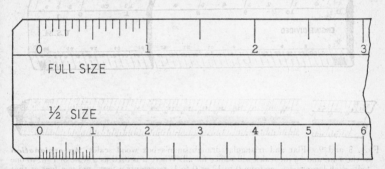

Fig. 6.—Typical draughtsman's scale detail with inch divisions instead of inches to foot, as in fig. 5.

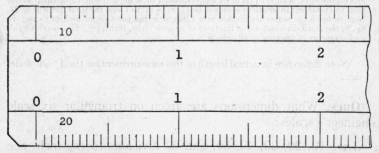

Fig. 7.—Typical *engineer's scales* detail showing scales with 10ths and 20ths of inch divisions.

Ques. On a ¾ inch = 1 foot how do you lay off a distance, say 2'-6"?

Ans. In fig. 5, from a given point as **A**, place the ¾ scale with division 2 at the given point, then the zero division on the scale will be at a distance of 2 feet. Now since the end space is divided into twelfths each representing inches on the ¾ scale, measure off six divisions and get the measurement AB = 2'-6".

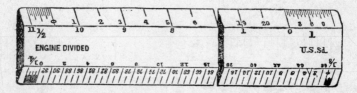

FIGS. 8 and 9.—Flat and triangular draughtsman's box wood scales. *An explanation* of the 1 in. and ½ in. scales will suffice for all. Where it is used as a scale of 1 in. to one foot, each large space, as from 0 to 12 or 0 to 1, represents a foot, and is a foot at that scale. There being 12 in. in one foot, the twelve long divisions at the left represent inches; each inch is divided into two equal parts, so from 0 to one division at the left of 9 is 9½ in. and so on. The 1 in. and ½ in. scales being at opposite ends of the same edge, it is obvious that one foot on the 1 in. scale is equal to two feet on the ½ in. scale, and conversely, one foot on the ½ in. scale is equal to six inches on the 1 in. scale; and 1 in. being equal to one foot, the total feet in length of scale will be 12; at ½ in. to 1 foot the total feet will be 24. Note in fig. 8 the scales are divided into 12ths or inches per foot for architect's use. In fig. 9, the small divisions are in fractions of an inch (8ths, 16ths, etc.) for draughtsman's measurements in drawing small objects.

Note difference in actual length of this measurement on the 1" = 1' scale, fig. 5.

Ques. What dimensions are given on triangular six scale engineer's scales?

Ans. 10, 20, 30, 40, 50, and 60 divisions to the inch. See fig. 7.

Ques. Are drawings sometimes made on scales larger than the object?

Ans. Yes.

In the case of a very small object such as a small watch, for clearness the drawing may be made two or three times larger. The scales being indicates as 2 : 1, 3 : 1, meaning twice actual size, three times actual size.

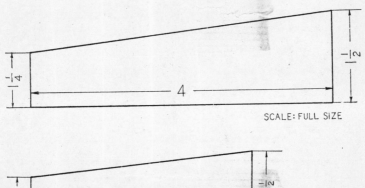

SCALE: FULL SIZE

SCALE: FULL SIZE

GRAPHIC REPRODUCTION SCALE

Figs. 10 and 11.—Graphic reproduction scale.

Ques. How is the scale affected on drawings reduced in size by photography?

Ans. The scale on the original would not apply to the reproduction.

Ques. What should be done in such cases?

Ans. The scale on the original (fig. 10) should be crossed out and a "graphic scale" of proportions corresponding to the reproduction added as in fig. 11.

Ans. The scale on the original would not apply to the reproduction

CHAPTER 3

Conventional Lines

A drawing is made up of different kinds of lines each having its own meaning, that is, certain characteristic lines are used to convey different ideas and draughting practice has been pretty well standardized as to lines which avoids confusion in the reading of blue prints.

A good working drawing will be made as simple as possible, using only such lines as are necessary to give all the information necessary for the mechanic. Moreover the reader will not have to puzzle over a mass of lines more complicated than necessary. The same thing holds for dimensions and other data: A good drawing is accurate and complete, though simple and therefore is easily understood ("read") by the mechanic.

The lines generally used on drawings are:

1. Solid

   a. Heavy ████████████████████

   b. Medium ────────────────────

   c. Light ────────────────────

   d. Irregular ～～～～～～～～～～

2. Broken

   a. Short dashes — — — — — — — — — —

b. Alternate long and short dashes ___ _ __ _ ___ _

c. Alternate one long and two short dashes.___ __ ___ __

d. Long dashes ___ ___ ___ ___

e. Alternate two dashes and space _ _   _ _   _ _

It must be quite evident that to be able to *read*, that is, to *understand* a blue print, it is essential to know the meaning of all these various lines.

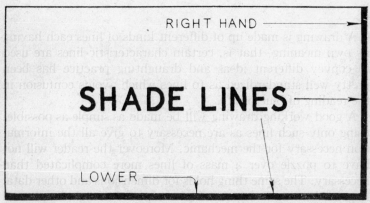

Fig. 1.—Drawing of a rectangle illustrating placement of shade lines. *Rule: Right hand and lower.*

The various lines are shown above and on page 17.

Ques. What use is made of heavy lines?

Ans. They are principally used as shade lines.

Sometimes used to represent a cutting plane instead of the dash and two dot lines.

Ques. Are shade lines necessary?

Ans. No.

On working drawings they are a waste of time. On an assembly drawing or pictorial drawing of a manufacturer's product they improve the appearance of a drawing and for such are permissible.

Ques. What is the rule for placement of shade lines?

Ans. "Right hand and lower."

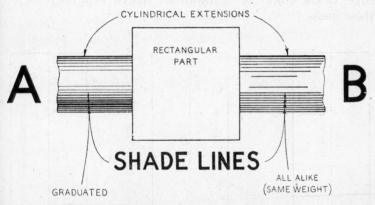

SHADE LINES

FIG. 2.—Forging with rectangular cylindrical contour illustrating important use of shade lines. Note that these shade lines are preferably as at A, graduated (each one of different "weight"—that is, width). Some draughtsmen make a sloppy job of shade lines by making them all same weight as at B.

Ques. What important use is made of shade lines?

Ans. To facilitate reading a drawing by bringing out pictorially a cylindrical surface.

For instance, fig. 2 shows a forging consisting of a rectangular central part having two cylindrical extensions. This is a semi-pictorial drawing and the shade lines show to the eye the cylindrical shape of the extensions. A more practical use of these shade lines is shown later in what is called a "sectional view."

Ques. What are the first lines the draughtsman lays down in making a drawing?

Ans. Axes or as they are usually called *center lines.*

Ques. Why are these lines drawn first?

Ans. It would be difficult to make the drawing as the various edges of the object being drawn are spaced with reference to these lines.

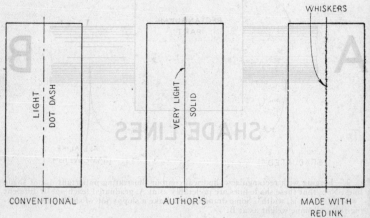

CONVENTIONAL   AUTHOR'S   MADE WITH RED INK

Figs. 3 to 5.—Various lines used for center lines whose characteristics are explained in the text.

Nearly all working drawings are of objects which are symmetrical with respect to some axes drawn through the center and are accordingly most easily drawn by first drawing such axes or center lines and then drawing the object so that its center coincides with the center line.

Ques. How are center lines represented?

Ans. By a long light dash and dot line or preferably by a light solid line.

The author's practice is solid center lines drawn very light to obtain proper contrast, thus avoiding confusion—the same with dimension lines.

Ques. What may be said of using red ink on tracings for center lines?

Ans. It is ridiculous.

The reproduction on the blue print is not sharp or well defined as when black ink is used. In fact it is considerably blurred—try it.

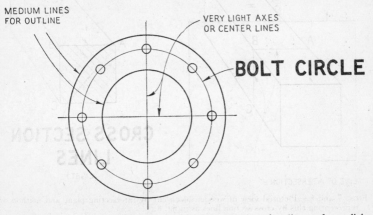

FIG. 6.—Lower side of a cylinder head illustrating application of medium and very light lines; also *bolt circle* which is an example of a curved center line.

Various methods of making center lines are shown in figs. 3 to 5. The conventional method, fig. 3, results in a waste of time in making the dots and dashes and they are not uniform even when made by the best draughtsmen. The red ink method, fig. 5, speaks for itself and looks like ————.

Ques. What use is made of medium solid lines?

Ans. They are used to outline all parts of an object.

Accordingly they predominate in number on a drawing and a skillful draughtsman will be careful to keep them uniform. In fig. 6 note the contrast between medium weight lines and very light lines used for outlining and center lines respectively.

Ques. What use is made of light solid lines?

Ans. They are used as section lines.

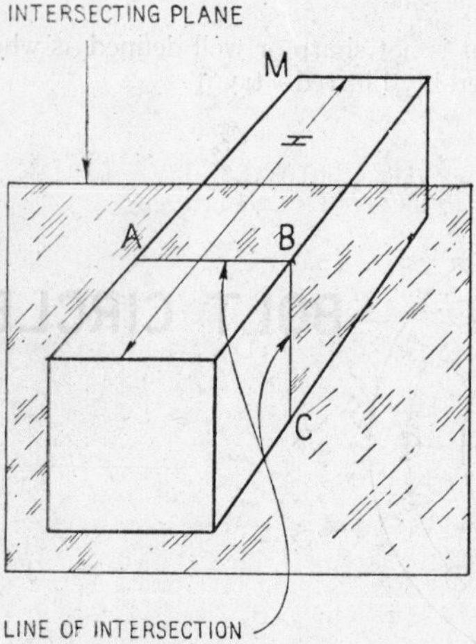

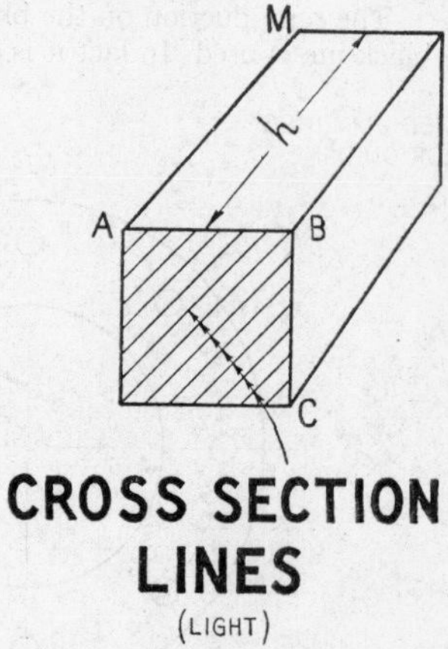

INTERSECTING PLANE

LINE OF INTERSECTION

CROSS SECTION
LINES
(LIGHT)

FIGS. 7 and 8.—Pictorial view of wooden block cut by intersecting plane and method of representing this by cross section lines as in fig. 8.

Ques. What are section lines?

Ans. A series of light solid parallel lines spaced close together to represent cut surface, that is, a surface cut by an intersecting plane.

This is illustrated in figs. 7 and 8. Fig. 7 shows pictorially an object of square section as a block of wood, cut by an intersecting plane along the line ABC.

If the block were sawed off in the plane through ABC the block would appear as in fig. 8. The cutting of the block is indicated by the cross section lines, fig. 8.

In the absence of the cross section lines there would be no graphical indication that the block was cut into two parts and in such case it would indicate that *h*, fig. 8, was the original length of the block instead of H (fig. 7).

Ques. What are the three kinds of sections usually drawn?

Ans. 1, cross section (as in fig. 8); 2, longitudinal section, and 3, oblique section.

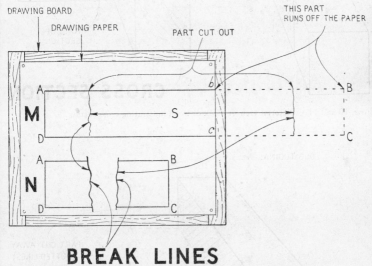

BREAK LINES

Fig. 9.—Diagram illustrating break lines and the expression "runs off the paper."

Ques. What is a cross section?

Ans. A drawing of an object showing that part cut by a plane at right angles to its longitudinal axis as in fig. 11.

Thus in figs. 10 and 11, fig. 10 shows the object (the same block of wood). Assuming it to be cut crosswise on line ABC the result is shown in fig. 11. Here the plane of the cross section indicated by the axis of section is at 90° to the longitudinal axis.

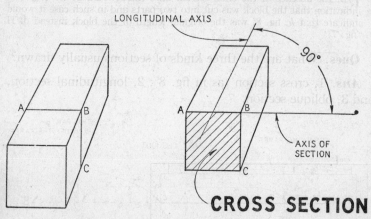

LONGITUDINAL AXIS

90°

A B

C

AXIS OF SECTION

A B

C

CROSS SECTION

Figs. 10 and 11.—Pictorial view of block of wood illustrating cross section.

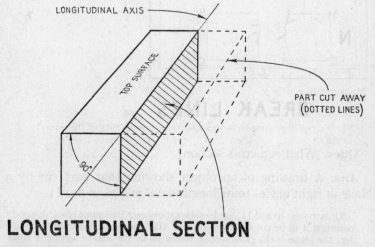

LONGITUDINAL AXIS

TOP SURFACE

PART CUT AWAY (DOTTED LINES)

90°

LONGITUDINAL SECTION

Fig. 12.—Pictorial illustrating longitudinal section.

Ques. What is a longitudinal section?

Ans. A drawing of an object showing that part cut by a plane passing through its longitudinal axis, as in fig. 12.

Here the part cut away is shown in dotted lines. Note that the plane of the section passes through the longitudinal axis and is at 90° to the principal surface of the object—here the top surface. Strictly speaking, a section shows nothing but the cut surface indicated by the section lines, but for simplicity and to show its position the pictorial drawing shows part of the object.

Ques. What is an oblique section?

Ans. A drawing of an object showing that part cut by a plane cutting the object at an *oblique angle** as in fig. 13.

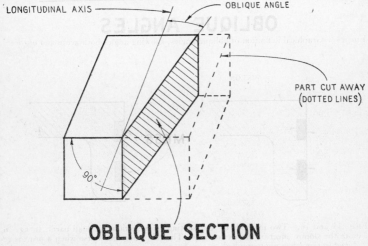

OBLIQUE SECTION

Fɪɢ. 13.—Pictorial illustrating oblique section.

---

*NOTE.—By definition an oblique angle is an acute or obtuse angle in opposition to a right angle; deviation from a right (90°) angle by any angle as in fig. 14.

Ques. What is an objectionable name given to the drawing of section lines?

Ans. Hatching*.

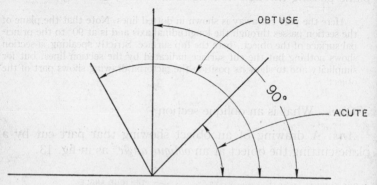

OBLIQUE ANGLES

FIG 14.—Graphical definition of oblique angles, showing angles both acute and obtuse.

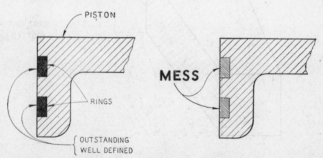

FIGS. 15 and 16.—Two methods of representing cross sections of small parts. In fig. 16, note the sloppy effect of the section lines. The effect becomes worse when a print is reduced in size when photographed.

---

*NOTE.—After diligent research, the name of the person guilty of profaning this word was not discovered. It should be restricted to the function of the hen in hatching chickens.

Ques. How is the section through a thin part as the shell of a boiler, or piston rings represented?

Ans. In solid black lines instead of section lines.

The reason must be obvious, as to section line such small parts the lines would have to be so close together as to result in a "mess." Compare figs. 15 and 16.

Ques. What does a heavy irregular line represent?

Ans. A break or part missing in the object.

Ques. What is the object of the break?

Ans. To economize space.

Otherwise if an attempt be made to show all of a very long object the drawing would "run off the paper" unless it be made on a very long sheet of paper. For example, fig. 9 shows a small drawing board.

At **M,** the draughtsman attempted to draw a long rectangle. He could draw only part of it AbcD. The remainder of the rectangle by the imaginary outline bBCc. This part bBCc is said in graphical slang to "run off the paper."

To overcome this difficulty *break lines* are used as at **N.** That is a whole section of the object is cut away and the two end pieces moved together as at **N,** as indicated by the *break lines.*

Moreover since the rectangle is of uniform *contour** it is completely represented at **N.**

The only thing missing, due to the break, would be a dimension indicating the distance between the ends AD and BC.

Ques. How are section lines drawn as to direction?

Ans. They are drawn usually inclined 30°, 45° or 60°.

---

*NOTE.—By definition, *contour* is: 1. The outline of a figure or a body; the line that bounds; periphery. 2. In civil engineering, the form of the ground surface with respect to its undulations.

Ques. Why at these inclinations?

Ans. Because they are conveniently drawn with the 45° or 60° triangles.

Ques. How are sections on adjacent parts distinguished?

Ans. By drawing the section lines at different angles as in fig. 17.

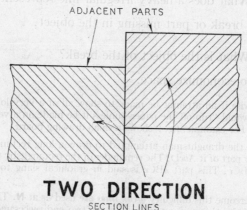

ADJACENT PARTS

TWO DIRECTION
SECTION LINES

Fig. 17.—Method of section lining two adjacent parts.

Ques. When two parts of an object on a section are separated how is it shown that they form one part?

Ans. By drawing the section lines over both parts in the same direction as at **A** and **B** in fig. 18.

Ques. What is the difference between a *section* and a *sectional view**?

---

*NOTE.—The term sectional view is frequently used incorrectly for *section*, hence note carefully the difference as given in the answer on the next page.

Ans. A section of an object shows nothing except that part cut by the intersecting plane. A sectional view shows in addition the outline of the object back of the section.

The distinction is shown in figs. 19 and 20. Here in fig. 19, note that nothing is shown but the section ABCD. To make a sectional view of this the outline of the object back of the section must be shown as in fig. 20.

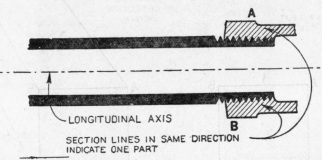

LONGITUDINAL SECTION

LONGITUDINAL AXIS

SECTION LINES IN SAME DIRECTION
INDICATE ONE PART

Fig. 18.—Longitudinal section of a pipe with screwed fitting illustrating that the metal at **A** and **B**, is one part as indicated by the section lines at **A** and **B**, drawn at the same angle. Note the thin walls of the pipe are in *solid black.*

Strictly speaking fig. 20 is a pictorial sectional view. Note that in these opening chapters the drawings are pictorial instead of orthographic as on blue prints, because anyone can understand a pictorial drawing. The *orthographic system* according to which all working drawings are made and which requires study is given in later chapters. Preceding this the reader should first understand all the conventional representations as standardized in draughting practice.

Ques. How are hidden lines indicated?

Ans. By dotted lines.

Fig. 22 shows a pictorial view of the visible parts of a cube. In fig. 21, the edges not visible in fig. 22 are shown by the dotted lines A, B, C. On blue prints numerous dotted lines are used to show parts not visible, but here good judgment should be used by the draughtsman to show only those necessary for the purpose of the drawing. Unnecessary complications on drawings make blue prints hard to read.

Ques. What other use is made of dotted lines?

Ans. They are sometimes used as projection lines on multi-view drawings (later explained).

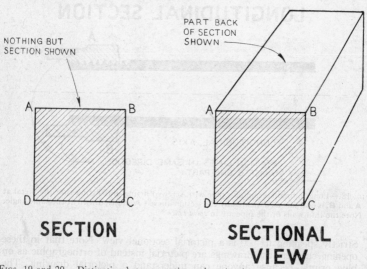

FIGS. 19 and 20.—Distinction between *section* and *sectional view* as explained in the text, fig. 20, pictorial representation.

Ques. Give another use for dotted lines.

Ans. They are very objectionably used for dimension lines.

Ques. How is a dimension indicated on a drawing?

Ans. By a very light line having a solid arrow at each end and a space along its length for the dimension as in fig. 23.

Here the distance between the points A and B is to be indicated. First two right lines A*a* and B*b* (light lines) are drawn and then the dimension line DL, with an arrow at each end touching the dimension limits A*a* and B*b*. The dimension line is broken at some point for the dimension, here 3.

Ques. Are dimension lines always made with dimension limits?

Ans. No.

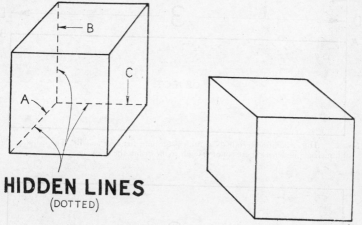

HIDDEN LINES
(DOTTED)

FIGS. 21 and 22.—Pictorial drawings of a cube with and without hidden edges shown illustrating dotted lines to represent hidden parts.

For a drawing like fig. 23, a better method of dimensioning is shown in fig. 24. Here no limit lines are used as the ends of the object serve the same purpose.

Ques. How is a very small dimension made?

Ans. By extending the dimension line and placing the arrows outside the limit lines as in fig. 25.

Here note that there is no room to put in the dimension between the limit lines. In such cases an extended dimension line is used with external arrows. This gives room for an arrow between the limits drawn from the dimension itself. On crowded drawings the dimension may be placed at any point where there is room.

Ques. Describe a very objectionable method of dimensioning.

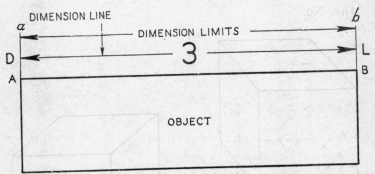

Fig. 23.—Dimension line terminals at dimension limit lines A*a* and B*b*. The usual method of dimensioning where there is not enough room within the drawing.

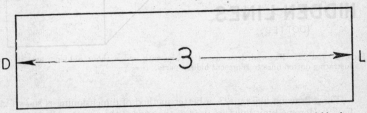

Fig. 24.—Method of avoiding dimension lines by placing the dimension line within the outline of the object.

Ans. Some draughtsmen for no conceivable reason use a dotted dimension line with arrows looking like sick "greater and less than" mathematical signs.

In the first place it takes longer to make a dotted than a solid line and moreover it is not a well defined indication like a solid line, to say nothing of the alleged arrow heads. Objections are shown graphically in fig. 26.

Ques. How are angular degrees indicated?

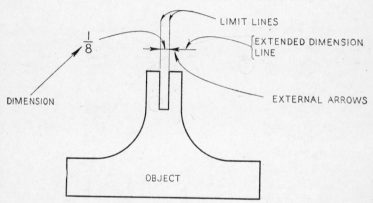

Fig. 25.—Method indicating very small dimensions.

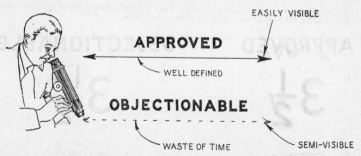

Fig. 26.—Approved and highly objectionable methods of drawing dimension lines and their arrow heads. It is sometimes necessary to employ an axe in exaggeration to drive some ideas home.

Ans. By a curved line with the angular dimension (degrees) placed between the two sides of the angle as in fig. 27.

Ques. In reading blue prints what precaution should be taken as to fractions?

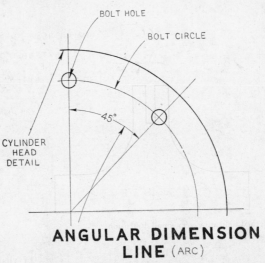

BOLT HOLE

BOLT CIRCLE

45°

CYLINDER
HEAD
DETAIL

ANGULAR DIMENSION
LINE (ARC)

FIG. 27.—Method of dimensioning an angle. Here a detail of the familiar cylinder head is shown as an example of indicating location of bolt holes.

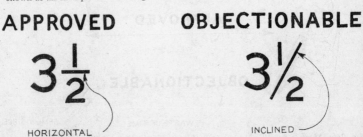

APPROVED   OBJECTIONABLE

$3\frac{1}{2}$ $3^{1/2}$

HORIZONTAL   INCLINED

FIGS. 28 and 29.—Approved and objectionable methods of writing fractions in dimensioning drawings.

ONE AND ONE SIXTEENTH

WOULD PROBABLY BE
READ, ELEVEN SIXTEENTHS

1 1/16   1 1/16

MADE WITH CARE   AS USUALLY MADE

FIGS. 30 and 31.—Result of writing mixed numbers with inclined division line when done in the usual careless and sloppy way. In some drawing rooms, these inclined lines are not allowed.

CURVED INTERSECTION LINE

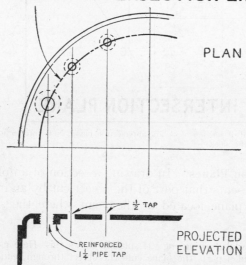

PLAN

½ TAP

REINFORCED
1¼ PIPE TAP

PROJECTED
ELEVATION

FIGS. 32 and 33.—Detail of vertical fire tube boiler upper tube sheet illustrating curved intersection line.

Ans. When the draughtsman writes fractions with an inclined division line (instead of horizontal as should be) be careful to avoid mistakes.

Figs. 28 and 29 show approved and objectionable methods of writing fractions. In the number here given 3½ there is not much chance of a mistake as no dimension would be given ³¹/₂. However, in such cases as one and one sixteenth it might be read as eleven sixteenths as in fig. 30.

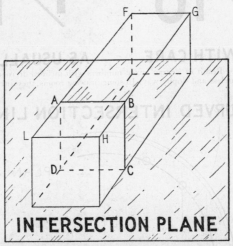

Fig. 34.—Pictorial of wooden block and intersection plane. Note intersection ABCD of the plane with the block.

Intersection Planes.—In drawing a section of an object the section represents that part of the object cut by an imaginary intersection plane located at the point where the section is drawn.

The pictorial drawing, fig. 34, plainly shows this. Here using dotted lines for hidden parts the plane cuts the object through section ABCD.

This is the same object (wooden block) as shown in fig. 7, but with hidden edges indicated by dotted lines.

Of course on a blue print there would be no pictorial drawing, but just an outline of one or more sides of the object (orthographic projection) would be given. Such view of the top side (LFGH, fig. 34) would appear as in fig. 35.

In such drawing the intersection plane appears as an intersection line because it is viewed from its edge in the direction of the plane. Hence, the section ABCD (fig. 32) would be called (in fig. 33) section cn line AB.

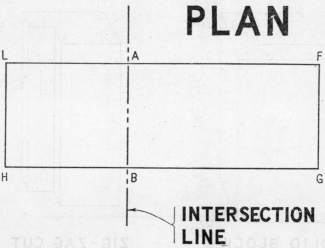

Fig. 35.—Plan drawing of the wooden block of fig. 34 illustrating intersection line.

Section lines may be:

1. Straight
2. Curved
3. Zig-zag
4. Irregular

depending upon the nature of the object and the sections desired.

Ques. What kind of line is used to represent an inter-section?

Ans. A medium dash, two dot line as in fig. 36.

Although intersection lines and lines of outline of parts are specified as medium, the careful draughtsman will make the intersection lines a little heavier to provide sufficient contrast that an intersecting line might not be taken for an outline line.

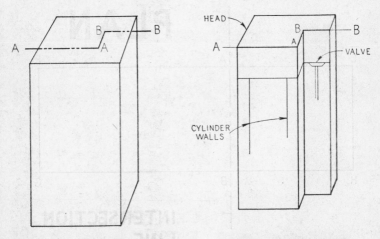

FIGS. 36 and 37.—Pictorial of a rectangular block illustrating zig-zag intersection line through a gas engine cylinder. Compare this with figs. 45 and 46, page 119.

For precision of location of the intersection it should not be unduly heavy.

Ques. When are curved intersection lines used?

Ans. On some objects of circular make up as for instance a boiler tube sheet as in fig. 32.

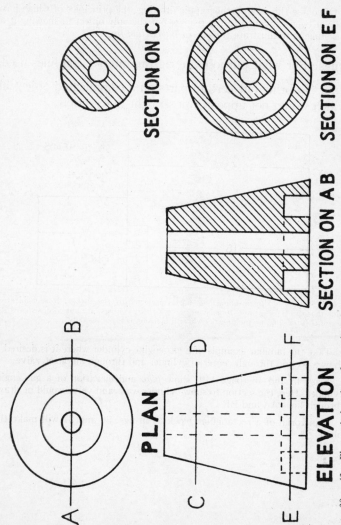

SECTION ON C D

SECTION ON E F

SECTION ON A B

PLAN

ELEVATION

Figs. 38 to 42.—Plan and elevation of cone shaped object illustrating notation for multi-sections.

Of course this is an orthographic drawing, the principles of which have not yet been explained to the reader, but the only object in showing it at this stage is to illustrate the *curved intersection line*.

Ques. For what purpose are zig-zag intersection lines used?

Ans. To bring out certain parts on a complicated object all of which would not appear in a straight line section.

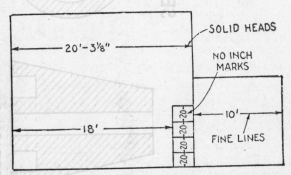

Fig. 43.—Method of dimensioning drawing as preferred by the author. Note solid arrow heads that can be seen; fine dimension lines which by contrast are not confused with the lines of the drawing; no inch marks where dimension is in inches only.

Take the familiar example of a gas engine cylinder where it is desired to show a section through center of cylinder and through an offset valve.

Figs. 45 and 46 (page 119) show *plan* and elevation of a gas engine cylinder. Here the section to show cylinder walls and valve would be drawn through lines AA and BB.

A pictorial of a rectangular block as in figs. 36 and 37 will make this plain.

CHAPTER 4

Conventional Representations
(Symbolic Conventions)

In addition to the conventional lines presented in the preceding chapter other standardized devices are used in conveying ideas on blue prints. These consist of various groupings of lines, symbols, abbreviations, etc.

Representation of Metals.—In the last chapter it was shown how a section is represented by parallel lines drawn close together.

By various combinations of light and heavy lines, spacing, etc., cross section lines will not only indicate a section but the kind of metal as well, such as:

1. Cast iron

2. Wrought iron

3. Steel

4. Composition

5. Lead or Babbitt

6. Aluminum

     etc.

The various arrangements of section lines to represent these various metals are shown in figs. 1 to 6.

Sometimes the plain light line sectioning as for cast iron, is used and the kind of metal specified. This results in a saving of time in making tracings.

Screw Threads.—There are several methods of representing screw threads. The one selected depending on the importance of

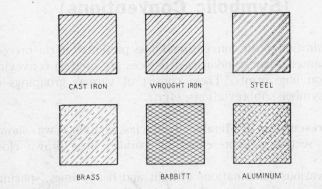

CAST IRON   WROUGHT IRON   STEEL

BRASS   BABBITT   ALUMINUM

Figs. 1 to 6.—Methods of indicating various metals by different arrangements of section lines.

the drawing and time available. Taking first an external thread as on a bolt it may be shown as in figs. 7 to 9. It takes some time to lay out and draw threads as at A, and accordingly they are usually drawn as at B. Such method as is shown at C, is not resorted to except on some hurry-up jobs.

Ques. What should be noted about internal threads drawn on sectional views?

Ans. The thread as seen back of the section slants opposite to the way it slants on the front or cut away side. See fig. 10.

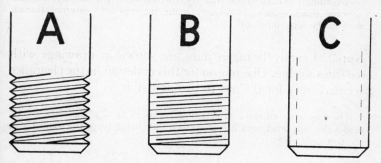

Figs. 7 to 9.—Various methods of representing screw threads.

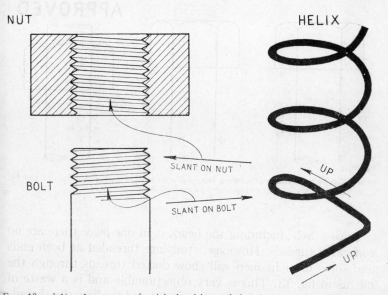

Figs. 10 and 11.—Appearance of a right hand internal thread as seen back of a section through a nut and an external thread. Note the internal and external threads slant in opposite directions. Why? The reason is shown clearly in the drawing of a helix in fig. 11.

Accordingly do not think that the threads are right and left handed. Some draughtsmen erroneously make internal and external threads slant in the same direction.

Nuts.—Usually hexagon nuts are shown in drawings with three sides visible. One reason for this in design, is the clearance space necessary for the nut to turn is visible.

They are easy to draw in this position as in fig. 12, the distance AB across the bolt head (which is same as a nut, being twice the diameter of the bolt or stud.

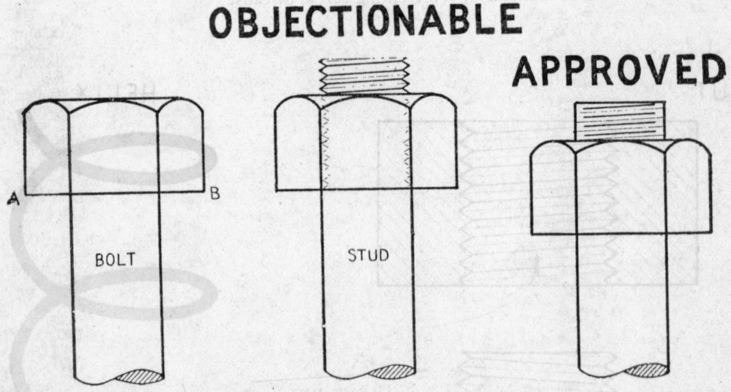

Figs. 12 to 14.—*Methods* of showing bolts and stud bolts. Fig. 12, bolt; figs. 13 and 14, objectional and approved methods of drawing stud bolts.

Since a bolt, including the head, is in one piece there are no concealed threads. However, studs are threaded at both ends and some draughtsmen will show dotted threads through the nut as in fig. 13. This is very objectionable and is a waste of time. The appearance is not improved and to show the threads is not necessary.

On most drawings nuts are shown as in fig. 14. The effect is more pictorial and anything that makes a drawing more pictorial makes its blue print easier to read.

It should be noted, however, that if the builder makes the nuts or bolts instead of buying them, there will be a detail of the nut looking at it in the direction H, with a dimension giving the distance between opposite sides or "between flats" as it is usually called because this is what the machinist must know when he makes the nut. See fig. 3, page 128.

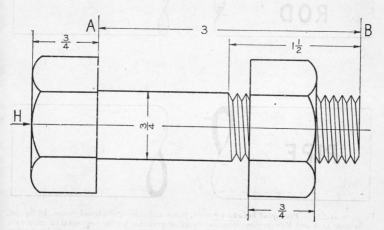

FIG. 15.—*Method* of dimentioning bolts. The drawing is practically pictorial and accordingly easily understood. It should be noted that the length of a bolt is given as AB, not the entire or overall length.

With this information he threads two side milling cutters on an arbor spaced to "distance between flats" and mills the nut by "straddle milling."*

In the absence of the bolt drawing a detail drawing of head, the "distance between flats" is stated on the bolt drawing.

―――――――――

*NOTE.—For a picture of this operation with full instructions see Audels Machinists and Tool Makers Handy Book by the author of this book.

From the foregoing it is seen that nuts are drawn one way by the designer and another way for the machinist. In most instances it is cheaper to buy nuts and bolts than to make them on the premises.

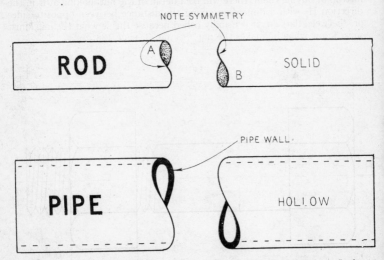

Figs. 16 and 17.—*Pictorial breaks* for rods, pipes and other cylindrical pieces. In fig. 16, the dots at A and B, represent irregular rough or granular fracture of metal in imaginary reality. Section lines would be out of place in representing such an irregular broken surface.

Breaks for Cylindrical Pieces.—Long pieces such as rods, pipes, pistons, etc., are usually shown in part to save space on the drawing. Instead of using the break line shown in Chapter 3, a more pictorial treatment is used as shown in figs. 16 and 17.

Abbreviations on Drawings.—A good rule for abbreviations is to use none that would be confusing. If confused as to an abbreviation in reading a blue print, consider the nature of the piece to be machined and the machining operations, which will be helpful in interpreting the abbreviations.

For Metals:

C.I. or I. Cast.............................. Cast iron

M. C. or Mal. Cast......................... Malleable casting

S. C. or St. Cast........................... Steel casting

Brs. Cast................................... Brass casting

Brz. Cast.................................. Bronze casting

T. S...................................... Tool steel

M. S...................................... Machine steel

For Processes:

Forg...................................... Forging

St. Stamp................................. Steel stamping

Press. st................................. Pressed steel

It should be understood that these abbreviations relate only to one part of the subject.

For every field such as carpentry, electrical work, foundry, shipfitters, etc., there are many conventions relating to each field.

For Machining Operations:

f. or fin.. Finish

Thr... Threads

D. or Dr... Drill

R. or Rad....................................... Radius

Fl... Fillet

Rm... Ream

CHAPTER 5

Pictorial Drawings

As an introduction to the system upon which "working drawings" are made, that is, by the descriptive method of *orthographic projection*, the reader should become familiar with the various systems of pictorial drawing. The three methods generally used may be classed as "fake perspective" as they show an object approximately as it appears when photographed.

Ques. Why are pictorial drawings not drawn in perspective?*

Ans. Such drawings present too many difficulties and accordingly take too much time.

Ques. Since working drawings are not pictorial drawings why is it desirable to study the different systems of pictorial drawings?

Ans. On blue prints, showing complicated objects, frequently a pictorial drawing of some detail is included as an aid to reading the blue print.

---

*NOTE.—By definition perspective is the art of delineating objects on a plane surface as they appear in reality to the eye.

Pictorial Methods of Representing Objects.—There are several methods of representing objects in drawings as by:

1. Perspective
2. Cabinet projection
3. Modified cabinet projection
4. Isometric projection
5. Anisometric projection

Of these methods, perspective is not treated here, as it is not used on blue prints.

Ques. What is the advantage of pictorial drawings?

Ans. Most of the object can be seen in one drawing. With the descriptive method used in working drawings only one side is seen in a single view.

Thus in the pictorial method the object is seen physically; with the descriptive method a mental impression of its appearance is conveyed by looking at several "views" separately.

Ques. What are the disadvantages of the pictorial method?

Ans. It requires too much time to make the drawing; difficult to fully dimension; some of the dimensions cannot be scaled from the drawings and all details cannot be fully shown.

Cabinet or Oblique Projection.—In this and other projection systems the lines of an object are drawn parallel to three axes.

Ques. How are the axes taken in cabinet projection?

Ans. The vertical and horizontal axes lie in a plane intended to appear to the eye as being at right angles to the paper.

The axes lie in planes at right angles to each other and are known as the horizontal, vertical and profile planes.

Ques. How are the axes usually designated?

Ans. As the **X**, **Y** and **Z** axes.

The arrangement is shown in fig. 1.

Ques. At what angle is the **X** axis drawn in cabinet projection?

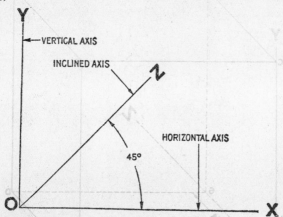

Fig. 1.—*Cabinet projection axes.* Note that the Z, axis is drawn 45° to the X, axis which distinguishes cabinet projection from modified cabinet projection in which the Z, axis is taken at other angles, in fact at any angle the draughtsman may select.

Ans. At 45° as in fig. 1.

Ques. How are horizontal lines parallel to the length of the object laid out?

Ans. Parallel to the horizontal axis in their actual sizes.

Ques. How about vertical lines parallel to the **Y** axis?

Ans. They must be drawn parallel to the vertical axis in their actual sizes.

Ques. What should be noted about lines parallel to the **Z** axis?

Ans. They are laid out in sizes of only one half that of the actual sizes.

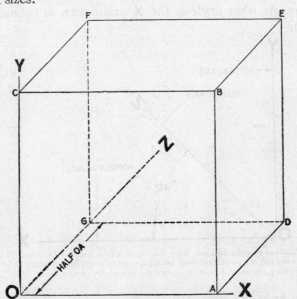

FIG. 2.—*Problem 1. Cabinet projection* of a cube. Note as in the case of an opaque object the invisible edges are indicated by dotted lines the same as on blue prints.

Problem 1.—To draw a cube in cabinet projection.

First draw the three axes, OX, OY, OZ, as in fig. 2. Lay off OA, and OC, on OX and OY, equal to side of the given cube, and complete the side by drawing CB and AB. On OZ, lay off OG, equal to ½OA. Through C, draw a line parallel to OZ, and through G, a dotted line parallel to OY giving the lines CF and GF. Similarly through points G, F, A and B, draw parallels to the axes, thus completing the cube.

In the drawing, the face ABCO, is regarded as lying in the plane of the paper, the face DEFG, as parallel and the other faces ABED and OCFG, as perpendicular to the plane of the paper.

The edges which would be invisible if the cube were made of opaque material such as wood, are represented by dotted lines.

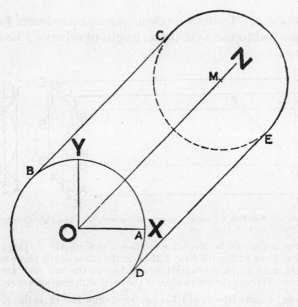

FIG. 3.—*Problem 2. Cabinet projection* of a cylinder with bases parallel to the plane of the paper.

Problem 2.—To draw a right cylinder with its bases in the XOY plane; length of cylinder 3 times the diameter.

This is the best position to draw a cylinder because the bases will be circles and the difficulty of describing ellipses avoided.

Draw the axes as usual.

With O, as center, fig. 3, and OA, equal to radius of cylinder, describe a circle. On OZ, lay off OM = 3 times OA (since length of cylinder = 3 times the diameter).

With same radius describe a circle through M, and draw tangents BC, and DE, thus completing the outline of the cylinder.

The portion of the circle about M, between C and E, is shown by dotted lines because it would be invisible if the cylinder were made of opaque material.

Problem 3.—To draw a prism enclosing a cylinder with its bases parallel to the YOZ plane; length of cylinder 3 times the diameter.

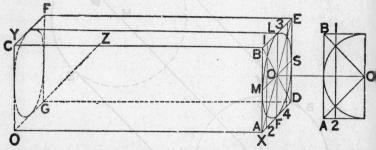

FIGS. 4 and 5.—**Problem 3.** *Cabinet projection* of a prism enclosing a right cylinder with its bases parallel to the Z plane.

Draw in the cube as directed in problem 1, making AD = ⅙ OA, as in fig. 4. Now, show half of the base ABED, in the plane of the paper as in fig. 5. Here, draw diagonals OB and OA, and describe the half circle tangent to the sides. Through the intersection of the circle with diagnols draw line 12.

In fig. 4 make B1 = ½ of B1 in fig. 5 and draw line 12, in fig. 4, and by similar construction line 34. Next draw diagonals AE and BD. The intersection of lines 12 and 34 with these diagonals will give four points together with points MLSF, through which to construct an ellipse representing the base of the cylinder as seen in profile constructing a similar ellipse at the other end and drawing the two tangents to the ellipses completes the outline of the cylinder.

Problem 4.—To draw a hexagonal prism inscribed in a right cylinder having a given length or altitude.

In construction fig. 6, describe a circle of diameter equal to diameter of the cylinder. Inscribe a hexagon. In fig. 7, lay off OF and OC, equal to O*f* and O*c*.

Transfer points *m*, *s*, obtaining **M**, **S**, and through **M** and **S**, draw lines parallel to **OZ**, and on these lines lay off **ME** = ½ *me*; MA = ½ *ma*, etc. Through the points thus obtained draw in the ellipse ABCDEF.

Similarly construct upper ellipse A′B′C′D′E′F′ at elevation

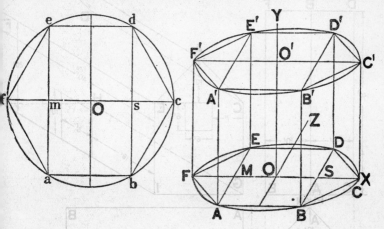

FIGS. 6 and 7.—*Problem 4. Cabinet projection* of a hexagonal prism inscribed in a right cylinder.

OO′ from the base and complete the cylinder. Join AB, A′B′, BC, B′C′, etc., and AA′, BB′, etc., thus completing outline of inscribed hexagonal prism.

Modified Cabinet Projection.—By definition this system is a method of projection similar to cabinet projection, but differing in that the **X** axis is not restricted to 45°. Also that lines parallel to the **Z** axis may be drawn on various scales, as half, two thirds or full size, etc. See figs. 10 to 12.

Ques. What is the object of these modifications?

Ans. To proportion the drawing to suit the space available.

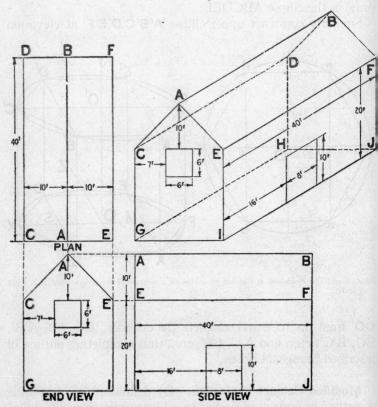

FIGS. 8 to 11.—*Cabinet projection* outline drawing of a barn and same drawn in orthographic projection.

Ques. Name a special provision.

Ans. Instead of inclining the **Z** axis to the right it may be inclined to the left as in figs. 12 and 13.

Isometric Projection.—By definition the word *isometric* means *equal distances* and as here applied, isometric projection is defined as *a system of drawing* with measurements on an equal

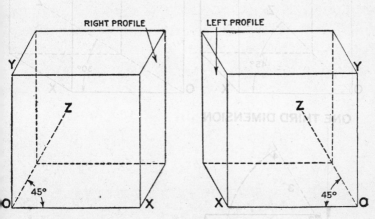

Figs. 12 and 13.—*45° cabinet projection* with *right* and *left* **profile.**

scale in every one of three sets of lines 120° apart and representing the three (**X, Y, Z**) planes of dimension.

Ques. State an important difference between isometric and cabinet drawings.

Ans. Isometric projection differs from cabinet projection in that none of the three planes lie in the plane of the paper as indicated in figs. 20 and 21.

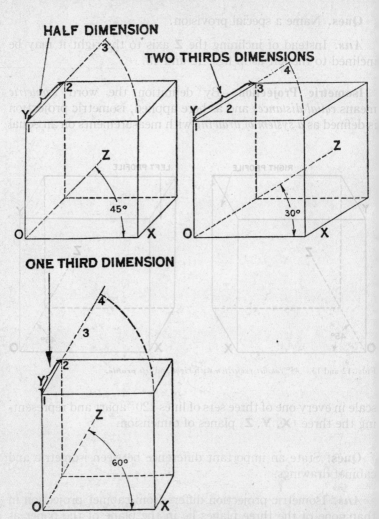

FIGS. 14 to 16.—**Approved proportions** for profile dimensions of 45°, 30° and 60°, Z axis inclinations.

Ques. How are isometric axes conveniently drawn?

Ans. With the aid of a T square and 30° triangle as in fig. 22.

Ques. How are dimensions laid off on an isometric drawing?

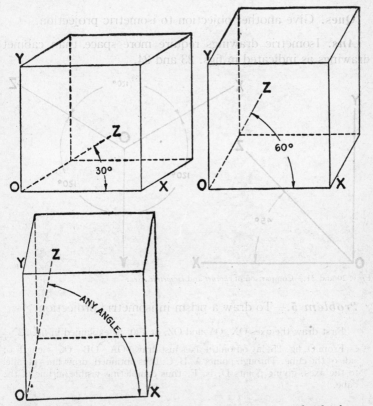

FIGS. 17 to 19.—*Modified* full dimension *cabinet projection* with axis at 30°, 60° and at any angle. Evidently these modifications render the system flexible with respect to space and clear representation of any special part of an object.

Ans. They are all laid off on the same scale without any shortening.

Ques. What difficulty is encountered in isometric drawing?

Ans. All circles become ellipses.*

Ques. Give another objection to isometric projection.

Ans. Isometric drawings require more space than cabinet drawings as indicated in figs. 23 and 24.

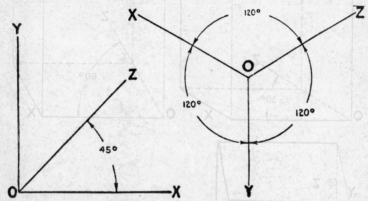

FIGS. 20 and 21.—Comparison of *cabinet* and *isometric axes*.

Problem 5.—To draw a prism in isometric projection.

First draw the axes OX, OY and OZ, at 120° as explained in fig. 22.

From O, fig. 25, lay off on the axes just drawn OA = OB = OC = length of side of the cube. Through points A, B, C, thus obtained, draw lines parallel to the axes, giving points D, E, F, thus completing visible outline of the cube.

---

*NOTE.—In cabinet projection, circles parallel to **XY** plane remain circles but become ellipses in the two other planes.

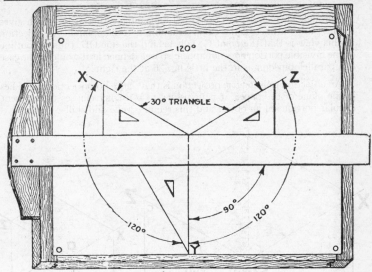

Fig. 22.—*Isometric axes* as conveniently laid out at 120° to each other with T square and a 30° triangle.

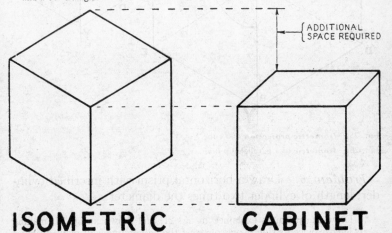

Figs. 23 and 24.—Comparison of *isometric* and *cabinet projection* as to relative space required.

Through D, E and F, draw dotted lines intersecting at G, which gives the invisible outlines of the cube, assuming it to be opaque. An objection to this view is that the point G, falls behind the line OB, thus the outline of the invisible portion does not appear so well defined as it would in the case of a parallelopipedon as in the little fig. 26 at the right.

An objection to isometric projection is that, since no projection plane lies in the plane of the paper, it is necessary to construct ellipses to represent circular portions of an object and this requires time and skill.

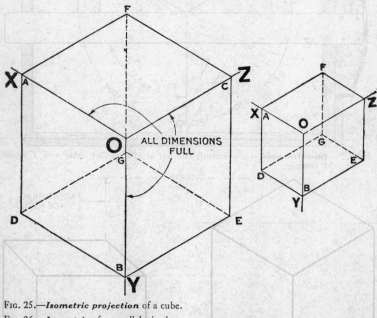

Fig. 25.—*Isometric projection* of a cube.

Fig. 26.—*Isometric* of a parallelopipedon.

Problem 6.—Draw a horizontal prism with inscribed cylinder; length of cylinder two times the diameter.

Draw the prism as explained in fig. 21, and drawn in fig. 27, making its length twice its side. Now construst the half end view in plane of paper (fig. 28); describe circle, diagonals and intersecting line 12.

Transfer from fig. 28 line 12 to fig. 27 and draw symmetrical line 34 and diagonals. The intersections, together with points MS, and LF, of axial lines through the center, give eight points through which construct ellipse.

Construct also a similar ellipse at other end of prism and join two ellipses with tangents, thus completing outline of inscribed cylinder.

Anisometric Projection.—This is a modified system. It differs from the cabinet system in that:

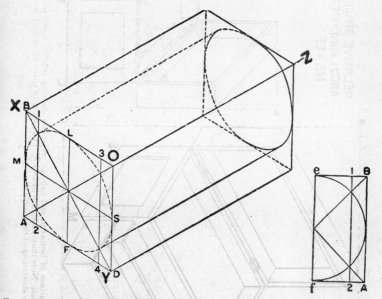

Figs. 27 and 28.—*Isometric projection* of a horizontal prism with inscribed cylinder.

1. None of its three planes lie in the plane of the paper.

2. Its axes lie at different angles.

3. Proportionate scales of measurement are used on the different axes.

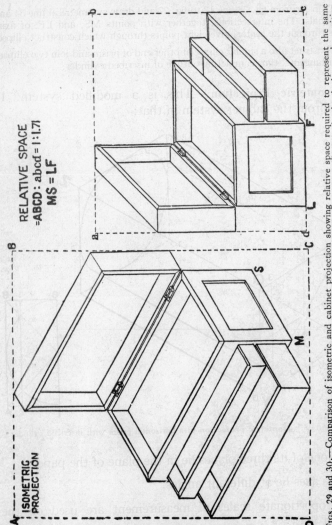

RELATIVE SPACE
=ABCD : abcd = 1:1.7!
MS = LF

ISOMETRIC
PROJECTION

FIGS. 29 and 30.—Comparison of isometric and cabinet projection showing relative space required to represent the same object drawn to same scale. Note that dimension MS = LF. The saving in space by cabinet projection is due to the position of the axes and the fore shortening of the profile dimensions.

Ques. What is the object of using a different scale for each axis and different angles?

Ans. The angles and proportions for the axes are so chosen that the drawing will very nearly approximate true perspective.

Problem 7.—Draw a cube in anisometric projection.

In fig. 31, axis MN makes an angle of 5°, and axis MP, an angle of 18° with the horizontal.

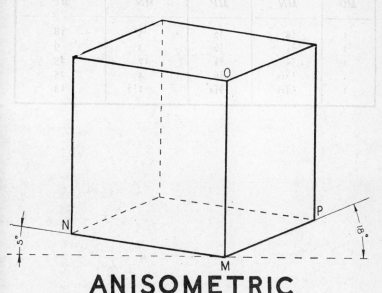

Fig. 31.—*Problem 7.*—*Anisometric* drawing of a scale. Isometric projection of a parallelopipedon showing completed dotted outline of invisible portion as compared with that of the cube fig. 25, in which part of the dotted line FG, falls behind OB.

From the accompanying table MO, is drawn to true scale, MN to ⅞ of true scale and MP, ½ of true scale. That is calling scale for MO 1, the fractions show relative sizes for MN and MP.

It is seen from this table that the angles and corresponding scales may be varied to suit the convenience of the draughtsman, so long as they do not defeat the purpose of the system, that is, to secure a nearer approach to true perspective.

Table of Anisometric Projection.

Proportion of Axes			Angles with Horizontal, Degrees	
MO	MN	MP	MN	MP
I	7/8	1/2	5	18
I	3/4	1/2	3	9
I	7/8	3/4	17	25
I	15/16	3/8	4	25
I	15/16	5/16	1 1/2	13

CHAPTER 6

Descriptive Drawings

This is that branch which is concerned with *the descriptive graphic method of representing points, lines, objects and the solution of problems relating thereto*. It is here popularly called descriptive drawings as another title for *descriptive geometry*.

The earnest student will do well to study this chapter as an introduction and preparation for the chapter following on *Orthographic Drawings*, which is the method used in making working drawings. The author believes such study will be very helpful in understanding orthographic drawings, a knowledge of which is necessary for "blue print reading."

The descriptive method of drawing is based on *parallel projections to a plane by rays perpendicular to the plane*.

If the plane be horizontal the projection is called the *plan* of the figure, and if the plane be vertical, the *elevation*.

The drawings are so made as to present to the eye, situated at a particular point, the same appearance as the object itself, were it placed in the proper position.

This descriptive method is also known as *orthographic projection* and in this chapter some of the basic principles are presented in preparation for taking up the subject at length in the chapters following.

Ques. What is projection?

Ans. A representation of any object on a plane.

Ques. How is the line of sight regarded so as to avoid pictorial drawing?

Ans. At an *infinite* distance in a perpendicular drawn to the plane of projection.

Ques. Since the point of sight is assumed to be at infinite distance what will be the direction of projecting lines drawn from different points of the object being projected?

Ans. They will be parallel with each other and perpendicular to the plane of projection.

Ques. What are projection lines?

Ans. Lines of sight.

Ques. How do lines of sight proceed from the eye when an object is viewed at a finite distance?

Ans. Radially.

The difference between radial and parallel lines of sight (lines of projection) is shown in figs. 1 and 2.

Ques. How are projection lines represented on a drawing?

Ans. By light dotted lines.

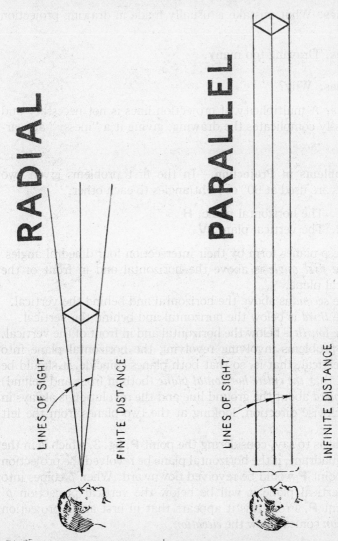

Figs. 1 and 2.—*Radial* and *parallel* lines of sight.

Ques. What mistake is usually made in drawing projection lines?

Ans. Drawing too many.

Ques. Why?

Ans. A multiplicity of projection lines is not necessary and uselessly complicates the drawing, giving it a "messy" appearance.

Problems in Projection.—In the first problems given two planes are used at 90° or right angles to each other.

1. The horizontal plane, **H**
2. The vertical plane, **V**

These planes form by their intersection four dihedral angles.

The *first angle* is above the horizontal and in front of the vertical plane.

The *second* is above the horizontal and behind the vertical.

The *third* is below the horizontal and behind the vertical.

The *fourth* is below the horizontal and in front of the vertical.

In problems involving revolving the horizontal plane into the vertical, that is, so that both planes coincide, it should be noted that *the entire horizontal plane* (both in front and behind) *is revolved* about the ground line and the revolution is always in a clockwise direction, looking at the two planes from the left side.

That is to say, considering the point **P,** fig. 3, which is in the first quadrant, if the horizontal plane be revolved the projection *p* of point **P** would be revolved downward. When *p* comes into the vertical plane it will be below the vertical projection *p'* of point **P**. From this it appears that in first angle projection the *plan* comes below the *elevation*.

Problem 1.—*Given the two projections of a point to find the point.*

In fig. 3,

Let p and p' be the projections of the point in the horizontal and vertical planes respectively. At p and p' erect ⊥s, by drawing lines from p and p' ⊥ to the H and V planes respectively.

The intersection P of these lines is at the point required.

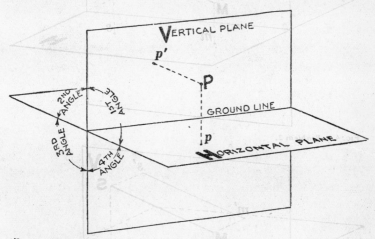

Fig. 3.—*Problem 1.*

Problem 2.—*Given the projections of the extremities of a line to find the line.*

This is simply an extension of problem 1.

In fig. 4

Let ms and $m's'$ be the projections of the extremities of the line in the H and V planes respectively.

Project as in problem 1, to locate the extremities M and S, of the line. Join M and S, giving MS, the line required.

Problem 3.—*Given the traces of a line to find the line.*

In fig. 5

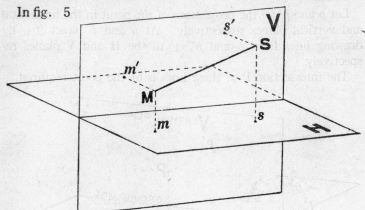

Fig. 4.— *Problem 2.*

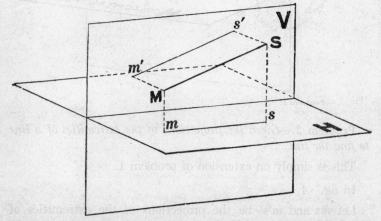

Fig. 5.—-*Problem 3.*

Let *ms* and *m's'* be the **H** and **V** traces respectively of the line.

From the points *ms* and *m's'*, the extremities of the traces, project as in problem 2 to locate the extremities M and S of the line.

Join M and S, giving M S the required line.

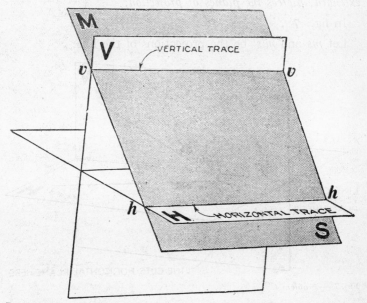

FIG. 6.—Intersection of a plane *MS*, with the *V* and *H* planes, showing horizontal trace *hh* and vertical trace *vv*.

Planes.—A plane is determined by its two *traces*, which are two lines cut on the *projection* planes.

If the plane be parallel with the axis its traces are parallel with the axis. Of these one may be at infinity; then the plane will cut one of the planes of projection at infinity and will be parallel with it. Thus a plane parallel with the plane has only one finite trace, that is the trace made by its intersection with the **V** plane.

If the plane pass through the 'axis both its traces coincide with the axis. This is the only case in which the representation of the plane by its two traces fails.

Problem 4.—*To locate the point in which a given straight line extended, pierces the planes of projection.*

In fig. **7** ,

Let *ms* and *m's'* be the projections of the line.

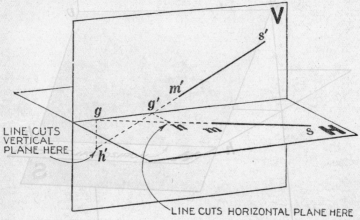

Fig. 7.—*Problem 4.*

Produce the vertical trace *m's'* until it intersects the ground line at *g'*, and at *g'* erect a ⊥ to the ground line in the **H** plane and produce it until it intersects the horizontal trace extended at *h*, the required point of intersection with the **H** plane.

By a similar construction the intersection *h'* with the **V** plane is obtained.

Problem 5.—*To find the distance between two points* M *and* S *in space.*

In fig. 8 ,

Let *ms* and *m's'* be the traces of a line joining the two points M, S.

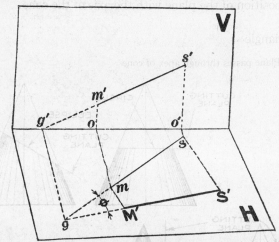

Fig. 8.—*Problems 4 and 5.*

From the ends of the vertical trace *m's'* erect ⟂s to the ground line *m'o* and *s'o'*, cutting the ground line at o and o' respectively. On the horizontal projection *ms*, erect ⟂s; *m*M' = *om'* and *s*S' = *o's'*.

Join the points M' and S'. The length of this line M'S' is equal to the length of the line MS (not shown) in space.

In order not to complicate the drawing, the line MS in space is not shown.

If the construction be accurate M'S' extended will cut *ms* extended at *g* the point of intersection with the **H** plane, as determined by projecting over from *g'* the intersection of the vertical trace with the axis.

The angle ϕ is the angle made by **MS** with the **H** plane.

Conic Sections.—By definition a conic section is *a section cut by a plane passing through a cone.*

These sections are bounded by well known curves, and the latter may be any of the following depending upon the inclination or position of the plane with the axis of the cone.

1. Triangle

Plane passes through apex of cone

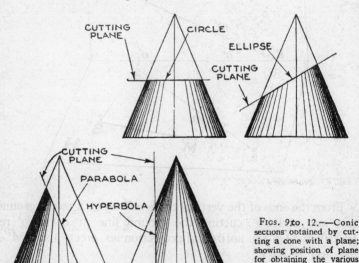

Figs. 9 to 12.—Conic sections obtained by cutting a cone with a plane; showing position of plane for obtaining the various sections.

2. Circle

Plane parallel with base of cone

3. Ellipse

Plane inclined to axis of cone

4. Parabola

Plane parallel with one element of cone

5. Hyperbola

Plane parallel with axis of cone

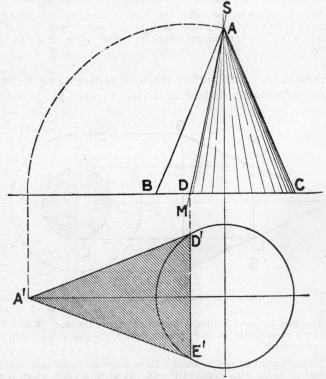

Figs. 13 and 14.—Surface cut by plane passing through apex of a cone—*triangle*.

These sections appear as straight lines in elevation, while in plan they appear (with exception of the triangle) as curves.

Problem 12.—Find curve cut by a plane passing through apex of cone as in figs. 13 and 14

Let ABC, be elevation of cone and MS, cutting plane passing through apex. Project point D, down to plan parallel with axis cutting base of cone at D' and E', obtaining line D'E', base of developed surface.

With D, as center and radius DA, equal to element of cone swing A, around to base line and project down to A'. Join A' with D' and E'. Then, A'D'E' is the developed surface or triangle cut by plane MS, with cone.

Problem 13.—Find surface cut by a plane passing through a cone parallel with its base as in figs. 15 and 16 .

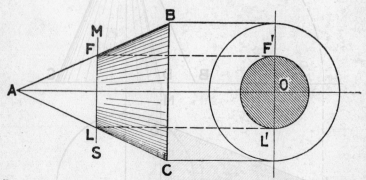

Figs. 15 and 16.—-Surface cut by plane passing through a cone parallel with its base—*circle.*

This may be found by simply projecting over to the plan. Where MS, cuts the element AB, as at F, project over to the axis of the plan and obtain point F'.

Similarly point L' may be found. These points are equidistant from the center O, hence with radius = OF' = OL', describe a circle which is the curve cut by plane MS, when parallel with base of cone.

Problem 14.—Find the curve cut by a plane passing through a cone inclined to its axis as in fig. 17.

In fig. 17, let the plane cut the elements OA and OB, of the curve at M and S, respectively. Project S, down to s', in plan giving one point on the curve. With S, as center swing M, around and project down to m', in plan giving a second point on the curve, $m's'$, being the major axis of the curve.

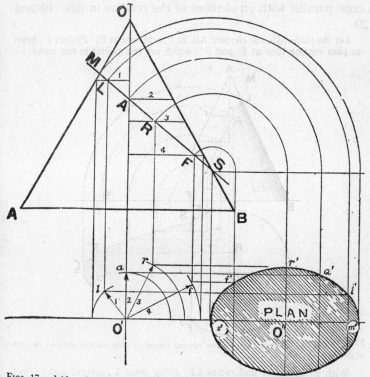

FIGS. 17 and 18.——Surface cut by plane passing through a cone inclined to its axis—*ellipse*.

To find the minor axis of curve, bisect MS, at R, and swing R, around to horizontal with S, as center and project down to plan. Through R, draw radius 3, and describe arc with radius 3, about O' as center. Where this cuts projection of R at r, project over to plan, intersecting the vertical plan projection of R at r'. O"r', is half the minor axis.

To find the projection of any other point as L, or F, proceed in similar manner as indicated, obtaining *l'*, or *f'*. The curve joining these points and symmetrical points below the major axis is an ellipse.

Problem 15.—Find the curve cut by a plane passing through a cone parallel with an element of the cone as in figs. 19 and 20.

Let the plane MS, cut element AB, at L, and base at F. Project F, down to plan cutting base at F' and F", which are two points in the curve.

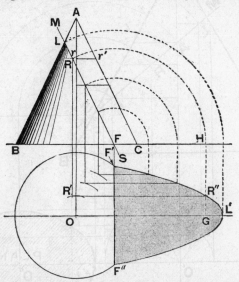

Figs. 19 and 20.—Surface cut by plane passing through a cone parallel with an element of the cone—*parabola.*

With F, as center and radius LF, swing point L, around and project down to axis of plan, obtaining point L' in the curve.

Now any other point as R, may be obtained as follows: swing R around with F as center and project down to plan with line HG.

Describe an arc in plan with a radius (=radius *rr'* of cone at elevation of point R), and where such cuts the projection of R at R'; project R' over to line HG, and obtain point R", which is a point in the curve.

Other points may be obtained in a similar manner. The curve is traced through points F′,R″,L′, etc., and similar points on the other side of the axis, ending at F″. Such curve is called a *parabola*.

Problem 16.—Find the curve cut by a plane passing through a cone parallel with the perpendicular axis of the cone, as in figs. 21 and 22

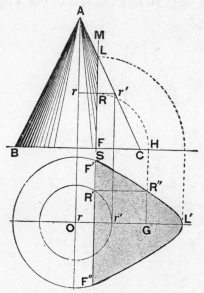

Figs. 21 and 22.—Surface cut by a plane passing through a cone parallel with the axis of the cone—*hyperbola*.

Let plane MS, cut element AC, at L, and base at F. Project F, down to plan cutting base at F′ and F″, which are two points in the curve. With F, as center and radius FL, swing point L, around and project down to axis of plan obtaining point L′, in the curve.

Now any other point as R, may be obtained as follows: Swing R, around with F, as center and project down to plan with line HG. Describe a circle in plan with radius rr' (= radius of cone at elevation of point R) and where this circle cuts the projection of R at R', project over to line HG, and obtain point R'', which is a point in the curve. Other points may be obtained in a similar manner.

The curve is traced through points F', R'', L', and similar points on the other side of the axis ending at F''. Such curve is called a *hyperbola*.

It will be noted that problems 15 and 16 are virtually worked out in the same way. In fact the text of one will apply to the other.

CHAPTER 7

Orthographic Drawings

All working drawings as on blue prints are made according to the method of orthographic projection.

The geometrical definition of **orthographic** is:

Of, or pertaining to perpendicular lines.

Hence by extension **orthographic projection** is:

Projection in which the projecting lines are perpendicular to the plane of projection.

If the student has studied the preceding chapter, he will find it much easier to understand the instructions here given.

Since the theory on which orthographic drawings are made is a little more complicated than cabinet or isometric projection, it is necessary to thoroughly understand the basic principles of the orthographic method in order to read blue prints. When a mastery of this is obtained, blue print reading will be found very easy.

To one not familiar with working drawings, they look like a "mess of lines" that give no idea of what they represent.

The experienced mechanic or draughtsman finds that his attention is not diverted by the numerous lines but that they guide him to picture the object which they represent.

As pointed out in the last chapter pictorial drawings are based on *radial* lines of sight—that is, radial lines of projection but orthographic drawings depend on *parallel* lines of sight.

Instead of considering the eye at an infinite distance for parallel lines of sight, it may be clearer to assume that the position of the eye is changed for each line so that it is directly in perpendicular line with each point of an object viewed. This is shown in fig. 1.

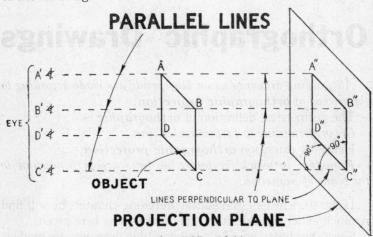

Fig. 1.—Diagram illustrating effect of parallel lines of vision.

Thus, let ABCD be the object. View each point by moving the eye to positions A'B'C'D' so that the line of vision will in each case be through the point and perpendicular to the projection plane, striking the latter in points A"B"C"D".

If these points were marked on the plane and the object moved perpendicularly to the plane, then the points ABCD of the object would coincide with points A"B"C"D" marked on the plane. Compare this with radial rays as in fig. 2 with eye in one position.

Ques. What is the radial projection effect in fig. 2 when object is between the eye and the projection plane?

Ans. The outline of the object on the projection plane is *larger* than the object as in fig. 2.

Ques. What is the effect when the projection plane is between the eye and the object?

Ans. The outline of the object on the projection plane is *smaller* than the object, as in fig. 3.

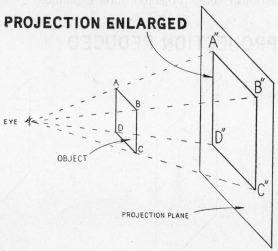

PROJECTION ENLARGED

Fig. 2.—Diagram illustrating effect of radial projections with object between eye and projection plane.

Ques. With parallel projection what is the effect of changing relative position of the object and eye?

Ans. The projection of the object on the plane is always the same size as the object as shown in fig. 4.

Accordingly, the daughtsman can scale the projections of an object and place the dimensions on the drawing as the perpendicular projecions are always the same.

Ques. When is the projection not the true size?

Ans. When the side of the object being projected is not parallel with the plane.

Ques. How is this overcome?

Ans. By projecting on an *auxiliary plane* parallel with the side of the object being projected (later explained).

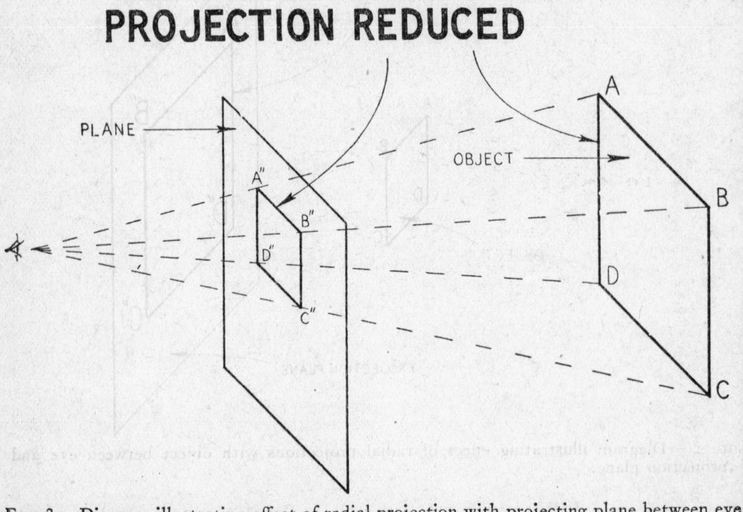

PROJECTION REDUCED

FIG. 3.—Diagram illustrating effect of radial projection with projecting plane between eye and object.

Orthographic Projection Views.—In the orthographic method, several views are required to completely show an object, the number required depending upon the shape of the object and the position of the views relative to each other will depend upon which quadrant is selected for the projection.

In explaining orthographic projection views in this section the illustrations show *second* and *third* angle projection.

For simplicity, self defining names are here given to the various views, although different names are preferably used for these views, thus:

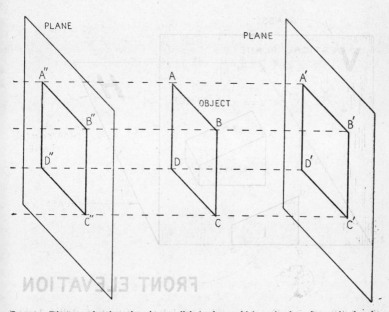

FIG. 4.—Diagram showing that in parallel (orthographic) projection the projection is always the same size as the side of the object projected irrespective of relative placement of object and plane.

1. Top view   known as   ***plan***
2. Bottom view   "   "   ***bottom plan***
3. Front view   "   "   ***longitudinal elevation***
4. Left side view   "   "   ***left end elevation***
5. Right side view   "   "   ***right end elevation***

From this it is seen that any view is either a ***plan*** or an ***elevation***.*

Ques. What is a plan?

Ans. A horizontal view of an object.

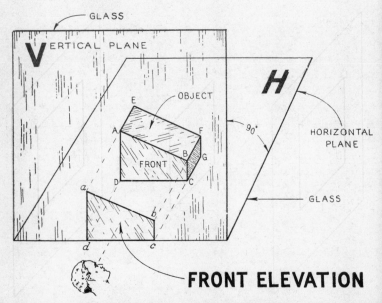

FIG. 5.—Rectangular object resting on horizontal plane and facing vertical plane. As shown the object is in the second quadrant. If the horizontal plane were shown above the object this would put it in the third quadrant.

---

*NOTE.—The practice especially of architects of calling a set of drawings (made up of both plans and elevations) "plans" of the building is erroneous and ridiculous in that it echoes *the power of suggestion*. This goes also for boat builders in speaking of the alleged "sheer plan" which in fact is a longitudinal elevation. However, in this case, they excuse it on the ground that after the drawing is made the lines of the drawing are laid down full size on a horizontal floor—for that matter the original drawing was made on a horizontal drawing board but that does not make it a plan. Accordingly "the power of suggestion knows no errors."

Ques. What is an elevation?

Ans. A vertical view of an object.

Views as Projected.—The various views are projected on imaginary projection planes, similarly as the projection of a picture on a camera plate or ground glass, with the difference that the orthographic projection lines are parallel and perpendicular to the surface instead of radial as in photography.

To illustrate, a clear pane of glass may be taken and for the first or front view, placed in front of the object, with the glass parallel to the surface of the object being projected.

In fig. 5, is shown a rectangular object with inclined top, the illustration shows this resting on the horizontal glass plane, placing it in the second quadrant. In front of the object is the pane of glass marked V, representing a vertical plane.

Now when an observer looks through the glass directly at the front of the object from a considerable distance, he will see only one side, in this case the side marked ABCD.

> The rays of light falling upon the object are reflected into the eyes of the observer, and in this manner as he sees the object, the pane of glass (vertical plane) evidently is placed so that the rays of light from the object will pass through the glass in *straight parallel lines* to the eye of the observer.

In reality the lines are not parallel but are radial. However, to meet the orthographic projection requirements they are taken as parallel which they would be in this case if the object were viewed at an *infinite distance*.

The rays of light (orthographic projection lines) from points ABCD of the object pass through the glass at points *a*, *b*, *c*, *d*. If these points *a*, *b*, *c*, *d* be connected by lines a view of the object as seen from the front is obtained which is called *front elevation*.

Ques. For the particular object shown in fig. 5, what may be said of the front elevation?

Ans. It is identical as to shape and size with the front side ABCD of the object.

That is, *ab*=AB; *bc*=BC, etc.; angle *dab*=angle DAB; angle *abc*= angle ABC, etc.

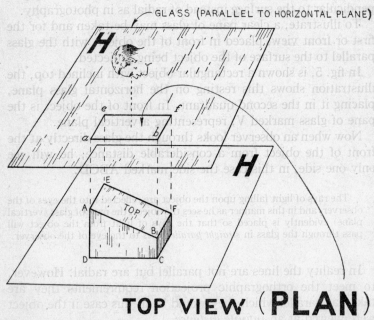

Fig. 6.—Projection of top of object to obtain top view (plan) *aefb*. Since the top is inclined the plan thus obtained is foreshortened.

Top View or Plan.—For this view place the pane of glass in a horizontal position above the object which is resting on the horizontal plane (drawing board) as in fig. 6.

Now looking at the object directly from above, the rays of light (orthographic projection lines) from corners AEFB of the top pass through the glass at points *aefb*. If these points *aefb* be connected by lines, a view of the object as seen from the top is obtained, which is called the top view, or preferably **plan**.*

Ques. In what quadrant is the object of fig. 6 as viewed?

Ans. It may be in either the third or fourth quadrants de-

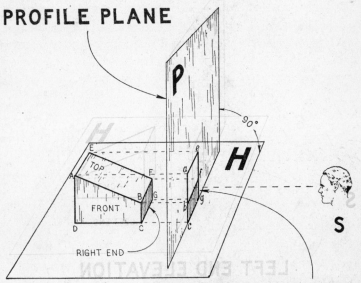

Fig. 7.—Projection of right end of object illustrating (right) profile plane.

pending upon the placement of the vertical plane which is not shown here.

---

*NOTE.—The word **plan** unqualified means *top* plan as distinguished from a plan of the bottom of an object.

Right End View (Elevation.)—Here the pane of glass is placed to the right of the object in a vertical position and parallel to the right side BFGC of the object as in fig. 7.

Here the pane of glass is marked P which means *profile plane* or plane from a side projection.

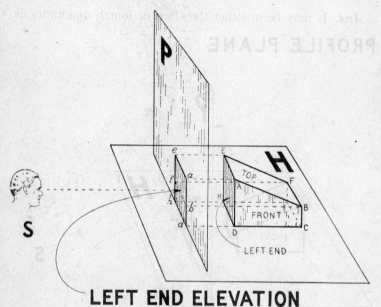

LEFT END ELEVATION

Fig. 8.—Projection of left end of object illustrating (left) profile plane and representation of invisible parts on elevation.

Now looking at the object directly from the right side (as position **S**) the rays of light (orthographic projection lines) from corners BFGC of the side also from AE (top of left side) pass through the glass at points *bfgc* and *ae*.

If these points be connected by lines, a view of the object as seen from the right side is obtained which is called the right side view or preferably right end elevation.

Ques. What is the peculiarity of the elevation?

Ans. The shape of the object is such that the entire surface visible does not lie in a plane parallel to the projection plane.

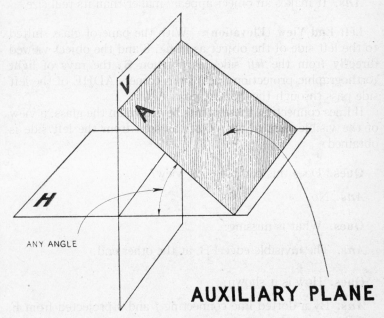

ANY ANGLE

AUXILIARY PLANE

Fig. 9.—Auxiliary plane. Note method of indicating the planes by lettering them **H**, horizontal; **V**, vertical, and **A**, auxiliary plane.

The points A and E, though located at the other end of the object are visible and accordingly form part of the right end view.

Ques. Does *aefb* show the top in its true size?

Ans. No.

Ques. Why?.

Ans. Because it is projected obliquely instead of at 90°.

Ques. What is the effect as to size of oblique projection?

Ans. It makes an object appear smaller than its real size.

Left End View (**Elevation**).—With the pane of glass shifted to the left side of the object as in fig. 8 and the object viewed directly from the *left* side (as position **S**) the rays of light (orthographic projection lines) from corners ADHE of the left side pass through the glass at points *adhe*.

If lines connecting these points be drawn on the glass, a view of the visible part of the object as seen from the left side is obtained.

Ques. Does this complete the view?

Ans. No.

Ques. What is missing?

Ans. The invisible edge FB, at the other end.

Ques. How is it shown?

Ans. By a dotted line connecting *f* and *b* projected from **F** and **B**.

The completed drawing is then called a *left side view* or preferably **a** *left end elevation.*

Projection of Oblique Surfaces.—Some irregular shaped objects will have a side that will not be parallel with any of the projection planes, that is, not horizontal, vertical or in the direction of the profile plane.

Ques. How is a true projection of an oblique surface obtained?

Ans. By projecting on an oblique or auxiliary plane such as shown in fig. 9.

Here the horizontal and vertical planes are marked **H** and **V**. The shaded

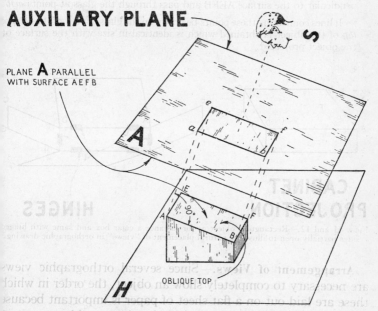

AUXILIARY PLANE

PLANE **A** PARALLEL
WITH SURFACE A E F B

OBLIQUE TOP

FIG. 10.—Projection of inclined side of object illustrating application of auxiliary plane to obtain true size projection.

plane marked **A** is laid out at the same angle as that of the surface to be projected so that the plane will be parallel with the surface.

Ques. Why should the auxiliary plane be parallel with the surface to be projected?

Ans. To obtain perpendicular 90° projection which is necessary to prevent distortion, giving a projection of the object in its true size and shape.

Thus, in fig. 10, the auxiliary plane **A,** is shown at such angle that it is parallel with the oblique surface, AEFB of the object. Now when the object is viewed through glass directly in line as position **S,** the rays of light (orthographic projection line) from corners AEFB of the object project perpendicular to the surface AEFB and pass through the glass at points *aefb.*

If lines connecting these points be drawn on the glass, a view of the *oblique top* of the object is obtained which is identical in size with the surface of the object projected.

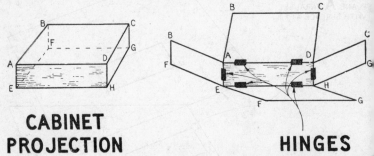

CABINET
PROJECTION   HINGES

Figs. 11 and 12.—Rectangular object as for instance a cigar box and same with hinged sides partially open to illustrate natural placement of "views" in orthographic drawing.

Arrangement of Views.—Since several orthographic views are necessary to completely show an object, the order in which these are laid out on a flat sheet of paper is important because improper grouping will render the drawing worthless.

To represent a solid object on a flat piece of paper is difficult. It can be shown only in part by *cabinet* or *isometric* drawings. Hence orthographic drawings are employed to fully show an object.

As will be shown later, the order of grouping will depend on the quadrant or angle of projection used.

First the arrangement universally used in this country, that is, ***third angle** projection*, will be explained.

For illustration a rectangular object like a cigar box will be shown in cabinet projection and then "unfolded" so that all views come into the plane of the paper.

Fig. 11 shows the box.

Now imagine the various sides hinged so they could open as in fig. 12.

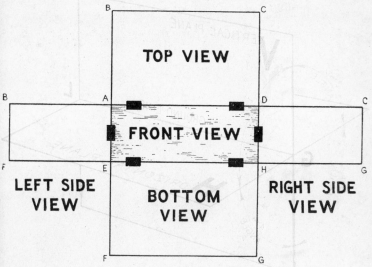

Fig. 13.—Five views of an object as drawn in orthographic projection.

Here they are shown partially open and the view shows pictorially how they open.

When the various sides have opened fully so that they are in the same plane as that of the front view, the assembly will look like fig. 13.

This represents the order of the views universally used here.

In fig. 13, starting with the front view, the sequence of view is as follows:

1. Top view is above front view
2. Bottom view is below front view
3. Right side view is at the right
4. Left side view is at the left

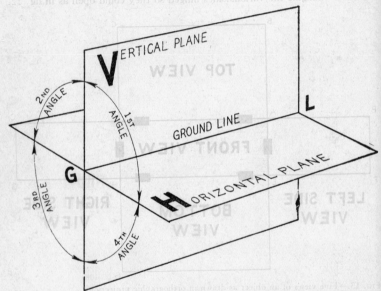

Fig. 14.—Intersecting vertical and horizontal planes illustrating the 4 quadrants or *angles* as they are usually called in stating in which angle the object is located for projection.

This arrangement of views is logical and is accordingly easily remembered. For such a simple object as the cigar box two views would suffice, but the other views here shown bring out the arrangement or order of views. This arrangement corresponds to *third angle* (quadrant) projection.

The Quadrants or "Angles" of Projection.—Since, as shown in the foregoing illustrations, the vertical and horizontal planes intersect, there will be four quadrants designated as angles in fig. 14. Evidently the object to be projected may be placed in any of these quadrants.

Ques. With respect to how the object is viewed what is the important difference between the first and third quadrants?

Ans. The object is viewed *direct* in the first quadrant and *through glass* in the third quadrant.

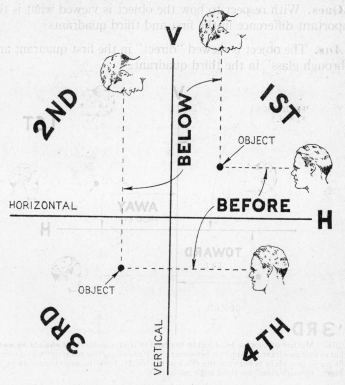

Fig. 15.—End view of vertical and horizontal planes illustrating how an object is viewed. *Rule: View the object directly **before** the eye or directly **below** the eye.*

Ques. How is the object viewed in any quadrant?

Ans. So that the line of sight is perpendicular to the projection planes.

That is to say, for instance, in first angle projection the object is always viewed as if directly *before* the eye or directly *below* the eye, as in fig. 15.

Ques. With respect to how the object is viewed what is the important difference in the first and third quadrants?

Ans. The object is viewed "direct" in the first quadrant and "through glass" in the third quadrant.

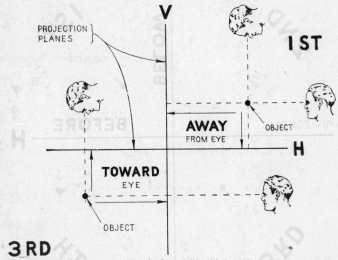

Fig. 16.—Method of viewing an object in first and in third quadrant. *It should be noted* that in first quadrant the object is between the eye and projection plane; in third quadrant the projection plane is between the eye and the object, thus the expression viewing the object "through glass" for third angle projection.

That is to say, the object is between the eye and the projection planes in the first quadrant, and the *glass* (projection planes) between the eye and the object in the third quadrant—"through glass."

Ques. What is the effect of the change in relative position of eye object and projection planes?

Ans. It changes the order or arrangement of the views.

Ques. How are the lines of an object projected in first and third angle projection?

Ans. In first angle projection, they are projected *away* from the eye to the projection planes beyond the object. In third angle projection they are projected toward the eye through the (glass) projection planes and traced thereon.

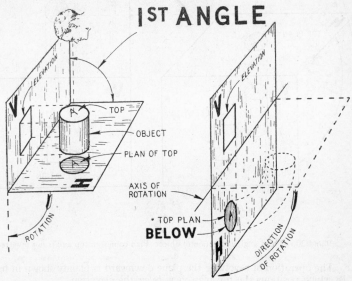

FIGS. 17 and 18.—First angle projection of object illustrating results obtained by this method. Plan comes below elevation and is inserted, that is, the plan at the bottom is plan of the top A.

This is clearly shown in fig. 16 for the projections on the vertical plane. The same conditions obtain for the projection on the horizontal plane.

Ques. In first angle projection why does the (top) plan come below the elevation?

Ans. Because the projection on the horizontal plane (plan) is revolved *downward* to bring it into the vertical plane.

Note in fig. 17 that the plan projected on the horizontal plane is the *top* of the object because the object is between the eye and the plane. Accordingly in such cases the projection will be that side nearest the eye.

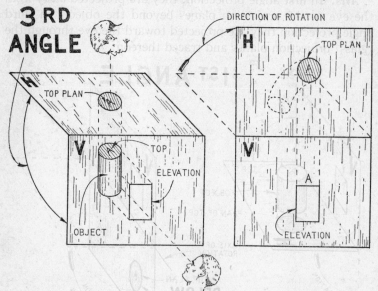

Figs. 19 and 20.—Third angle projection of object. Plan comes on top and is not inverted.

The operation of revolving the plane downward is plainly shown in fig. 18 which positions the top plan view *below* the elevation.

Ques. In third angle projection why does the top plan view come *above* the elevation?

Ans. Because the projection on the horizontal plane is a plan of the top and this is revolved *upward* to bring it into the vertical.

Thus in fig. 19, a cylindrical object is shown in the third quadrant with its projections on the **H** and **V** planes.

In viewing the object with the planes between the eye and the object, that is, object "through glass" it is clearly seen in fig. 19 that the top of the object which is the end nearest the **H** plane and the one projected on the **H** plane.

Similarly the elevation is projected on the **V** plane as shown.

Now in revolving the **H** plane into the vertical, the rotation is upward as shown by the arrow in fig. 20.

From figs. 19 and 20, it must be evident that in third angle projection the top plan comes *above* the elevation.

End Views in First Angle Projection.—The differences to be noted in first and third angle projection is the reversal in the positions of the various views. This has just been explained in the case of *plan* and *elevation*, and it remains to show the reason for reversal of the end views, that is, in first angle projection.

1. Right elevation comes on *left* side
2. Left elevation comes on *right* side

Considering now projection in the first angle where the object is always placed between the eye and the glass (projection plane), fig. 21, shows a cylindrical object as projected on the *vertical* and left **profile** planes.

Carefully note that the **profile** *plane* is at 90° to the vertical plane and at 90° to the horizontal plane.

Ques. In first angle projection of end views how does line of sight project?

Ans. It is projected away from the eye to the end of the object *nearest* the eye and thence to the profile plane.

Thus in fig. 21, if the observer view say point *a* of the object and the line of vision be continued straight to the profile plane, it would locate point *a'* thereon. Clearly then the projection on the *left* profile plane must be the projection of the *right end* **A**, of the object nearest the observer and remote from the left profile plan. Accordingly in first angle projection the *right* end view appears on the drawing at the *left* side.

Ques. Why does the *right* end view appear on the *left* side of the elevation?

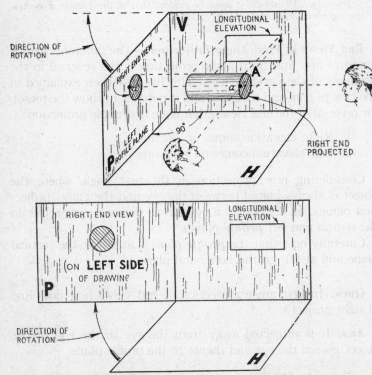

FIGS. 21 and 22.—First angle projection of cylindrical object illustrating why *right* end view comes on *left* side of drawing.

Ans. If the profile plane be rotated 90° in the direction shown in fig. 21, so that it lies in the vertical plane the right end view is rotated around to the left side as shown in fig. 22.

Ques. In first angle projection why does the left end view appear on the right side of the elevation?

1ST ANGLE

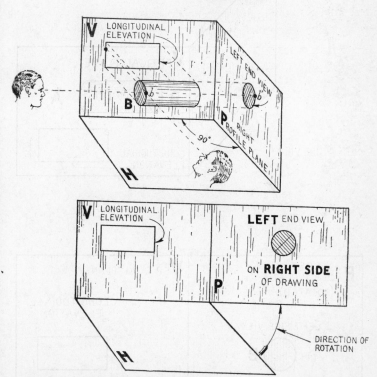

FIGS. 23 and 24.—First angle projection of cylindrical object illustrating why *left* end view comes on *right* side of drawing.

Ans. Similarly as for the right end view, it is because of the observer's position and the direction of rotation of the profile plane.

Thus, in fig. 23, the line of sight is projected to that end of the object nearest the observer thence to the profile plane.

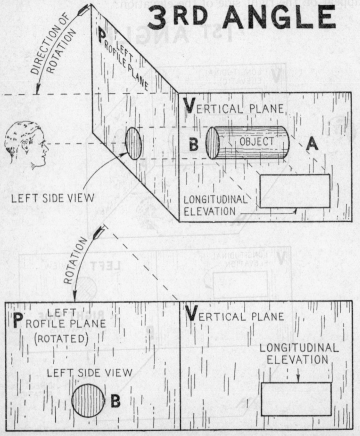

FIGS. 25 and 26.—Third angle projection on left profile plane.

Accordingly, if (in fig. 23) the observer view say point *b*, of the object and the line of vision be continued straight to the right profile plane, it would locate point *b'* thereon.

Clearly then the projection on the right profile plane must be the projection of the left end **B**, of the object nearest the observer and remote from the right profile plane.

Accordingly in *first angle projection*, the left end view appears on the drawing at the right side. This is shown in fig. 24. Note rotation of the profile plane as indicated by the arrow, that is, 90° to bring it in the vertical plane.

End Views in Third Angle Projection.—In orthographic drawings using third angle projection, end views and in fact all the views appear in their logically correct place. That is to say with respect to the end views.

In *third* angle projection

1. Right elevation comes on *right* side
2. Left elevation comes on *left* side

Considering now third angle projection where the object is always viewed "*through glass*," that is, the imaginary projection planes (assumed to be transparent as if made of glass) are always placed between the eye and the object as indicated in fig. 16.

Ques. In third angle projection of end views how are the lines of an object projected?

Ans. They are projected from the object toward the eye to the "*glass*" or projection plane and traced thereon.

In fig. 25 for a left side view note observer at left and profile plane (glass) between observer and the object.

Ques. When the profile plane is rotated into the vertical plane why does the left end view come on the left?

Ans. Because it is the nearest or left end B, of the object that is projected as clearly shown in the illustrations.

Note it is not the direction in which the profile rotates, but the particular end that is projected to the profile plane, that is, in this case, it is the left

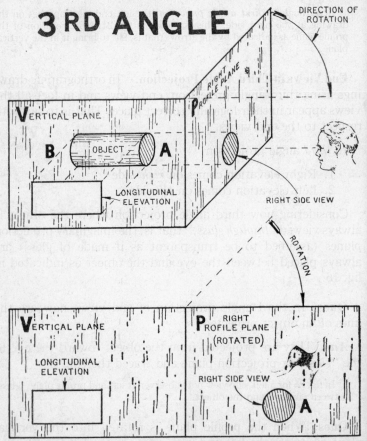

Figs. 27 and 28.—Third angle projection on right profile plane.

end **B,** that is projected instead of the opposite or remote end **A,** as would result in first angle projection.

Ques. How is the right side view projected?

Ans. As shown in fig. 27.

Here note, as for all third angle projection, that the projecting plane is between the observer and the object.

Accordingly, as viewed in fig. 27 the side A, of the object which is nearest the observer is projected to the intervening right profile plane. For this reason, when the profile plane is rotated into the vertical plane the right side view comes on the right side as plainly shown in fig. 28.

Bottom and Back Views.—These views for either first or third angle projection, are projected according to the same basic principles as have been applied at such great length to the other views. It seems, accordingly, unnecessary to give additional instructions.

Second and Fourth Angle Projection.—In a study of these projection quadrants it will be found that—

1. For second quadrant, plan and elevation lie *above* ground line.

2. For fourth quadrant, plan and elevation lie *below* ground line.

Ques. Why are the second and fourth quadrants seldom used in practice?

Ans. Because in revolving the H plane into the vertical, the plan views become *inverted*.

This is evidently objectionable and since otherwise the drawings are identical with those of the first and third quadrants there is no reason for using the second and fourth.

Ques. Show why in second angle projection the plan is inverted and below the elevation.

Ans. In fig. 29 since the projection on the vertical plane is of the end A, nearest the plane, evidently when the horizontal plane is rotated upward into the vertical as in fig. 30, the plan will become above the ground line as shown.

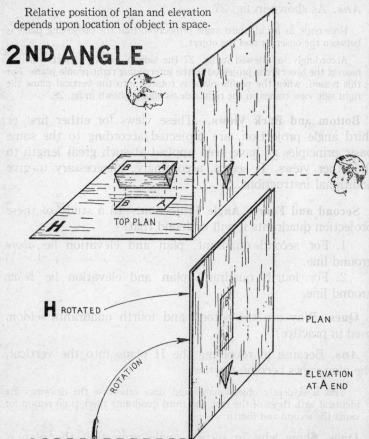

Relative position of plan and elevation depends upon location of object in space.

Figs. 29 and 30.—Second angle projection of a wedge shaped object illustrating that plan comes *below* elevation and is *inverted*.

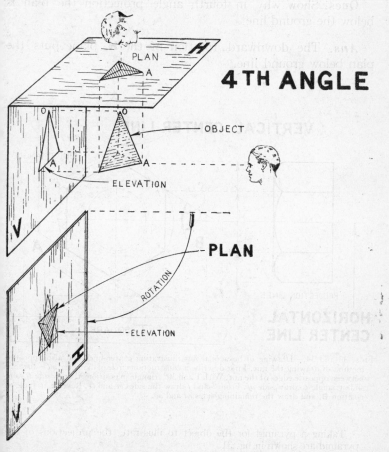

PLAN

A

4TH ANGLE

O   O

OBJECT

A   A

ELEVATION

V

PLAN

ROTATION

ELEVATION

H

V

Figs. 31 and 32.—Fourth angle projection of a pyramid illustrating that both *plan* and *elevation* come below ground line.

elevation will be of the side farther from the plane is indicated by edge OA. On rotation the plan comes above the elevation and by examining figs. 31 and 32 it can be seen how the plan becomes inverted

Ques. Show why in fourth angle projection the plan is below the ground line.

Ans. The downward rotation of the **H.** plane puts the plan below ground line.

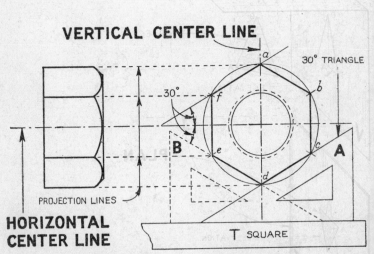

Figs. 33 and 34.—Drawing of hexagonal nut illustrating center lines and also approved method of drawing the nut. First describe a construction circle of diameter ad = distance between opposite edges of the nut. With T and 30° triangle in position A, draw side dc, and slide triangle to draw side af. From b and f draw the sides bc and fe. Reverse triangle to position **B**, and draw the remaining sides ed and ab.

Taking a pyramid for the object to illustrate, the projections of the pyramid are shown in fig. 31.

Since the object is viewed direct for the elevation, the projection of the elevation will be of the side remote from the V plane as indicated by the edge OA. On rotation the plan comes above the elevation and by comparing figs. 31 and 32 it can be seen how the plan becomes inverted.

Sections.—Sometimes an object to be drawn is of such shape that it cannot be clearly represented by a plan and elevation. In such case, the parts which do not appear properly in these drawings are better represented by a *section*, or *sectional view*.

Ques. What is a section?

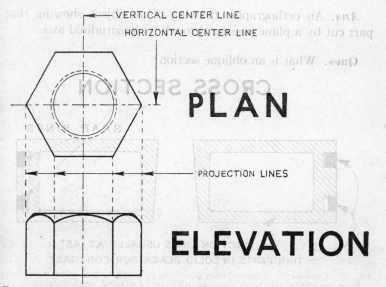

VERTICAL CENTER LINE

HORIZONTAL CENTER LINE

PLAN

PROJECTION LINES

ELEVATION

FIGS. 35 and 36.—Drawing of the hexagon nut shown in figs. 33 and 34 in a vertical position illustrating that here a *plan* and *elevation* are required instead of the *elevation* and *end view* shown in figs. 33 and 34.

Ans. An orthographic drawing of an object as it would appear if cut through by an intersecting plane. A section shows nothing but the part cut by the intersecting plane.

Ques. What are the three kinds of sections usually drawn?

Ans. 1. Cross section; 2, longitudinal section and 3, oblique section, classed according to the angle of the cutting plane.

Ques. What is a cross section?

Ans. An orthographic drawing of an object showing that part cut by a plane at right angles to its longitudinal axis.

Ques. What is a longitudinal section?

Ans. An orthographic drawing of an object showing that part cut by a plane passing through its longitudinal axis.

Ques. What is an oblique section?

CROSS SECTION

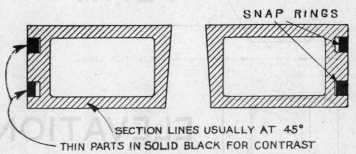

Fig. 37.—Cross section of engine piston illustrating sectioning by lines and in solid black. What two lines would change this cross section into a sectional view?

Ans. An orthographic drawing of an object showing that part cut by a plane cutting the object at an oblique angle.

Ques. What is a sectional view?

Ans. An orthographic drawing in which the parts of an object cut by the intersecting plane appear part in section and part in full view.

The object of this is to save time and make the drawing easier to read

Ques. How is a section through a thin part, as the shell of a boiler, usually represented?

Ans. In solid black instead of section lines.

Fig. 37 shows a *cross section* of a piston and illustrates the use of solid black for thin parts such as piston rings. If such parts were section lined they would not come out sharp and well defined as with the solid black section.

In sections which cut through separate and adjacent parts, these parts are distinguished by drawing the section lines of the second part at a different angle than those of the first part as in fig. 38.

CROSS SECTION
WITH ADJACENT PARTS

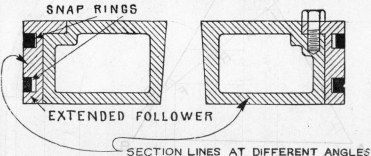

SNAP RINGS

EXTENDED FOLLOWER

SECTION LINES AT DIFFERENT ANGLES

Fig. 38.—*Cross section* of engine piston with extended follower (ring carrier) illustrating method of *section lining adjacent parts* to show that they are not integral. How could this be changed into a *sectional view* by drawing only two lines?

Fig. 39 shows an *oblique section* and illustrates triple projection from the cutting plane MS. It also illustrates projection in part *by revolution*, that is, in obtaining the section distances on the horizontal axis are obtained by revolving points, as LARF, in the cutting plane around S, as a center and projecting downward. Then from the vertical and horizontal projections at the right, points on the perimeter of the section as l'a'r'f' are obtained. Such constructions are problems in *descriptive geometry* which will be treated in a later chapter.

Fig. 40 illustrates a *sectional view*. Drawings of this kind are made of objects whose construction is the same on each side of a center line or axis.

Evidently here it would be a waste of time to show everything intersected by the cutting plane in section, because section lining is tedious requiring extra time and it is difficult to space the section lines equally. Moreover by showing part of the object in *view*, a better idea is obtained of its appearance and extra details can be shown in the view portion which would not appear in the section portion, for instance the split portion of the ring.

Directions of View for Sectional Views.

For an unsymmetrical object it is important to know the direction in which the

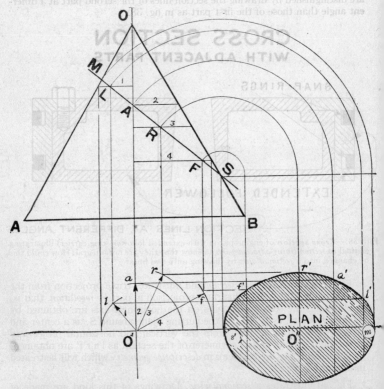

Fig. 39.—*Oblique section* of a cone on the line MS making an oblique angle with the axis OO.

sectional view is viewed. This is indicated by arrows at the
end of the line representing the cutting plane as shown pictorially in figs. 41 and 42.

Thus the arrows **AA,** indicate that the object is viewed in the direction
L, toward the smaller end of the object and the arrows **BB,** in the direction
R, toward the larger end.

Sectional views at **AA** and **BB** would appear respectively as at **L** and
R in figs. 43 and 44.

SECTIONAL VIEW

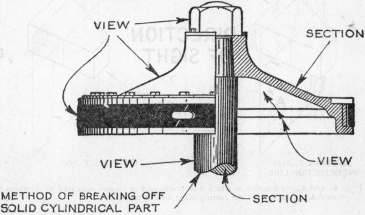

VIEW

SECTION

VIEW

VIEW

SECTION

METHOD OF BREAKING OFF
SOLID CYLINDRICAL PART

Fig. 40.—*Sectional view* of a mushroom type piston showing portions in view and in section; also method of breaking off the cylindrical rod.

Sections on Zig-Zag Intersection Planes.—A section is not
always taken along one straight plane, but is often taken along
zig-zag planes or even a curved intersecting surface, that is, the
intersecting plane may be offset or become a curved surface if
by doing so, the construction can be shown to better advantage.
Figs. 36 and 37 also page 38.

Number of Views Required.—This depends upon the nature of the object to be represented. In any case there should be enough orthographic projections, sections and detail drawings to completely represent the object in all its parts. This is necessary that the man in the shop may construct the object

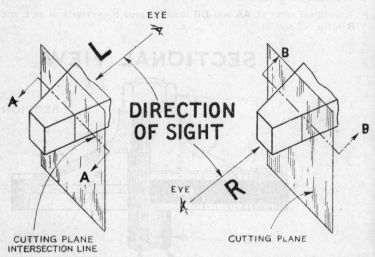

Figs. 41 and 42.—Direction in which a sectional view is viewed indicated by direction of arrows AA, at the ends of the cutting plane intersection line.

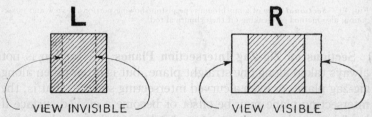

Figs. 43 and 44.—Appearance of sectional view with respect to the direction in which it is viewed. These are sectional views at **AA,** and **BB,** of figs. 41 and 42, **L** and **R** here indicate directions of sight as given by the same letters in figs. 41 and 42.

without loss of time in asking questions, etc. The blue print should give all the information required by the mechanic.

In the case of a complicated object sometimes a cabinet or isometric

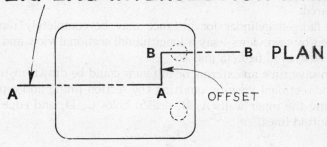

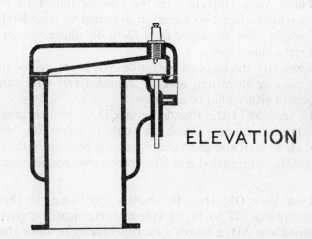

FIGS. 45 and 46.—Section of gas engine cylinder on zig-zag intersection line **AABB**. Note offset AB. The zig-zag line, fig. 45, indicates that part of the section is on line **AA** and part on line **BB**.

drawing in addition to the orthographic projections is helpful. With such addition the mechanic can more easily read the blue print and avoid a misconception of the general appearance of the object to be constructed.

Usually two views as plan and elevation suffice for symmetrical objects but for most irregular shapes additional views are required.

A flanged cylinder for instance may be completely represented by two views—say a longitudinal sectional view and an end view as in figs. 45 and 46.

To save time an external or full view could be drawn instead of the sectional view by omitting the section lining and representing the inner walls A, B, drilled holes C, D, and edge F, by dotted lines.

Three View Objects.—In the case of numerous irregular shapes more than two views are required to completely show the object. For instance, figs. 47 to 49 illustrates an object requiring three views.

Evidently the inclined back side AB, is not visible in either the plan or elevation, and the rounded end CD, cannot be shown in either plan or end view.

If, instead of the rounded end CD, it was rectangular as CD'D (dotted lines) the object would be completely shown by two views plan and end view. Evidently because of the inclined side AB, and rounded end CD, three views are necessary.

Four View Objects.—By slightly modifying the three view object of figs. 47 to 49, by cutting a corrugated groove in the inclined side AB, a fourth view is necessary to show the corrugations in their actual shape.

Thus in figs. 50 to 53, the actual shape of the side *no* of the groove *mnop* is shown by adding a fourth view or *section* on line LF.

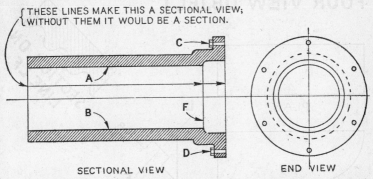

FIGS. 45 and 46.—A flanged cylinder or symmetrical object which may be completely represented by two views. When time is limited a full view would be made instead of the sectional view.

THREE VIEW OBJECT

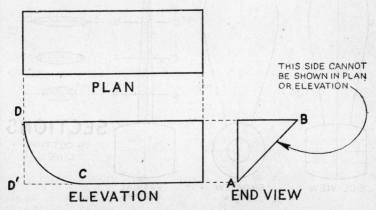

FIGS. 47 to 49.—Irregular shaped object requiring *three views*.

FOUR VIEW OBJECT

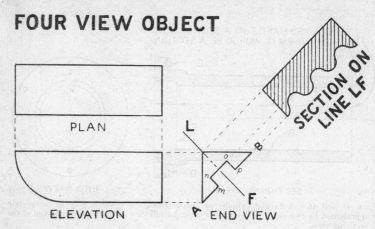

PLAN

ELEVATION

END VIEW

SECTION ON LINE LF

Figs. 50 to 53.—Irregular shaped object requiring *four views*.

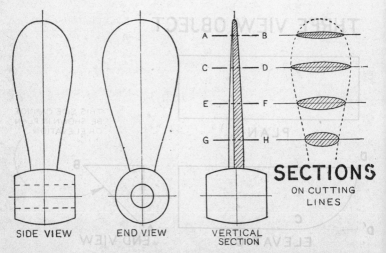

SIDE VIEW

END VIEW

VERTICAL SECTION

SECTIONS ON CUTTING LINES

Figs. 54 to 57.—Drawing of a propeller wheel requiring more than *four views*.

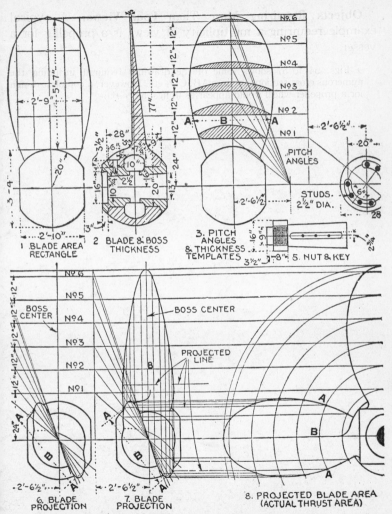

FIGS. 58 to 65.—Fully dimensioned working drawing of a built up propeller requiring a *multiplicity of views* including *many sections*.

Objects Requiring More Than Four Views.—A typical example requiring a multiplicity of views is a propeller for a vessel.

Figs. 54 to 57 shows some of the drawings required including the numerous cross sections on lines AB, CD, etc. However, a complete design for a propeller wheel would appear as in figs. 58 to 65.

CHAPTER 8

Working Drawings
(Blue Prints)

A working drawing usually in the form of a blue print is simply an orthographic drawing fully dimensioned and containing any other data necessary for the mechanic to do the job indicated without asking any questions.

He is not supposed to ask questions as that would indicate that he lacked ability to read blue prints, that is, working drawings.

Ques. What is most important on a working drawing?

Ans. The dimensions.

There should be a dimension for every part necessary to the mechanic to do the required work.

Ques. What should be included with several measurements of adjacent parts?

Ans. An overall measurement.

Ques. Why?

Ans. It is a check on the adjacent measurement and avoids adding the several measurements to get the overall distance.

Thus in fig. 1, note there are seven dimensions for adjacent parts of a two crank shaft. The overall dimension is necessary for the machinist to know how long the shaft should be between ends, that is "overall."

Ques. Is a dimension which spans several dimensions of adjacent parts necessarily an "overall" dimension?

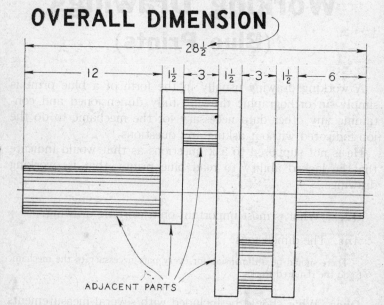

Fɪɢ. 1.—Longitudinal view of two throw shaft illustrating *overall dimension.*

Ans. No, in the sense that it does not cover the entire length of the object.

Thus in fig. 2, dimension A (5 in.) gives the length of threaded and unthreaded part of the bolt but not thickness of the head. Dimension B, is the actual overall dimension.

Ques. What has been put on the drawing, fig. 2, that is not necessary?

Ans. The abbreviation "hex."

Hex is abbreviation for hexagon. It is not necessary because the view of head is sufficient to show that the head is hexagonal.

Ques. What very important dimension has been omitted from the drawing?

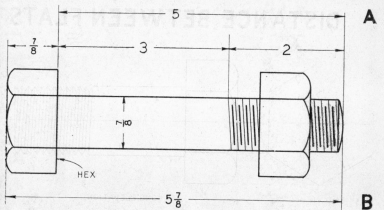

FIG. 2.—Drawing of bolt illustrating A, dimension covering several adjacent dimensions, and B, overall dimension.

Ans. The "distance between flats" of the head.

Ques. What is understood by "distance between flats"?

Ans. The distance between two opposite and parallel sides of the head or nut, as shown in fig. 3.

As previously explained, the machinist must know this distance in spacing right and left side milling cutters, which machine the sides of the head in pairs.

Ques. What should not be put on drawings of parts to be machined and why?

Ans. Inch marks (″) because they are not necessary. They clutter up the drawing and obscure the dimensions; moreover putting an inch mark after each dimension is a ridiculous waste of time.

Even a greenhorn would know that dimensions on a blue print such as a drawing of some small article as a watch or clock or some reasonably small machine part are not in feet or yards, but in inches.

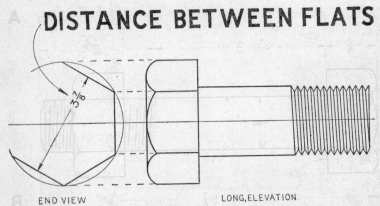

DISTANCE BETWEEN FLATS

END VIEW   LONG, ELEVATION

FIG. 3.—Method of dimensioning a bolt head or nut. It's not the major diameter that the machinist is interested in, but *the distance between flats*, because this gives him the required spacing in assembling *r* and *l* side cutters in the arbor of the milling machine.

Ques. In special cases to prevent any mistake in omission of inch and foot marks, what should be placed on the drawing?

Ans. The notation: All dimensions in inches and fractions thereof unless otherwise specified. This should go near the title of the drawing under the scale.

Ques. What should be considered in dimensioning a drawing?

Ans. The effect of location of dimensions upon ease of reading the drawing.

Thus, figs. 4 and 5 show a plan and elevation of a cylinder head, with all necessary dimensions for machining. Note here diameters are always clearer when shown on an elevation than on a plan. Accordingly only one, that of bolt circle, is shown on plane and the three other diameters on the elevation. The parts to be finished are marked *f*.

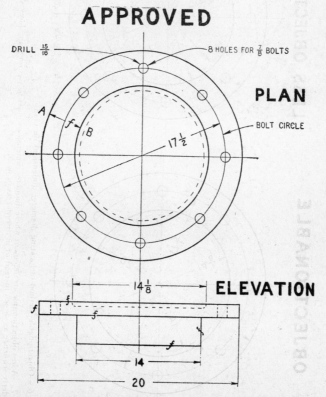

Figs. 4 and 5.—Proper location of dimensions for easy reading of drawing. Put dimensions for the various diameters on elevation rather than on plan. Fig. 6 shows why.

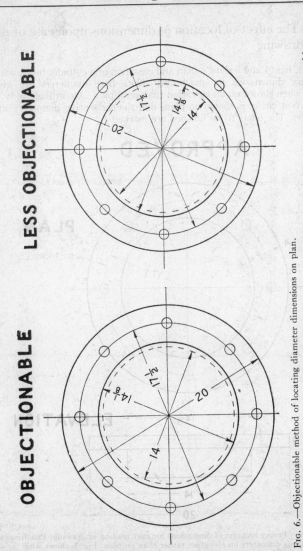

OBJECTIONABLE

LESS OBJECTIONABLE

Fig. 6.—Objectionable method of locating diameter dimensions on plan.

Fig. 7.—A less objectionable arrangement where diameter dimensions must be put on plan. They should be arranged in some orderly sequence as shown instead of in disorder as in fig. 6.

In reading the plan note that the top of the head is to be finished from A to B, the depressed part of the head from B to center being left rough.

Fig. 6 shows the result of putting dimensions for all diameters on the plan. It's a jumble of dimensions put on at various angles tending to cause mistakes.

Another criticism of fig. 6 is that the dimensions are not put on in an orderly way. That is, if they must appear on a plan a better arrangement is shown in fig. 7, but this still leaves much to be desired and shows that numerous diameter dimensions should not be put on a plan.

APPROVED

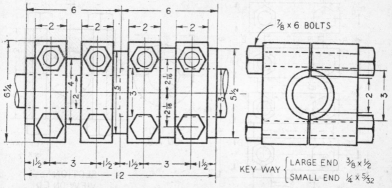

FIGS. 8 and 9.—Shaft coupling as designed by the author for yacht **Stornaway II**. It consists of two castings of square and cylindrical section around the shaft by eight bolts.

Full Views.—Working drawings may be made of many objects with symmetrical form by full views only, no sections being necessary.

A familiar example of the use of full views is the shaft coupling shown in figs. 8 and 9.

Here the object is completely shown by a longitudinal view and end view. This is a coupling for a marine engine whose shaft is larger in diameter than the propeller shaft with which it connects. Note the dimensions of these shafts are 3 and 2 inches respectively. The keyways dimensions are specified instead by being dimensioned direct owing to the smallness of the parts.

The dimensions for bolt lines are referred to the *center line* because they must be spaced the same distance each side of the center line.

Ques. What other way could working drawings be made of the shaft coupling of figs. 8 and 9?

OBJECTIONABLE

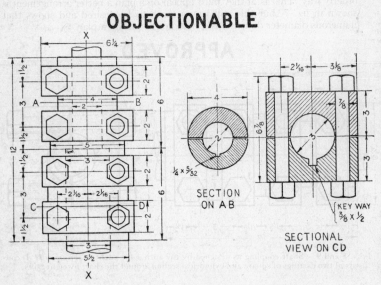

FIGS. 10 to 12.—Objectionable way to show the shaft coupling of figs. 8 and 9.

Ans. The coupling could be shown by the longitudinal view of fig. 8 and two cross sections as in figs. 10 to 12.

Ques. What is the criticism of this method (figs. 10 to 12)?

Ans. Although it shows the construction very clearly, it is objectionable on the ground that it is a waste of the draughtsman's time.

Ques. In fig. 9 did the draughtsman forget to describe dotted circles showing the 4 and 5 inch round portions as dimensioned in fig. 8?

Ans. No.

Ques. How would the pattern maker know that these sections were not square instead of round?

Ans. His common sense.

A pattern maker is a man of considerable intelligence; otherwise he couldn't make patterns. The draughtsman has indicated with the large circle in fig. 9 that the section at the end is round and this is enough in itself for the pattern maker to infer that the other sections are round.

Ques. What was the draughtsman's chief reason in omitting the dotted circles indicating round sections?

Ans. To simplify the drawing and make it easily readable.

By inspection, it is seen that all this drawing is intended to show is size of holes for shafts, bolts and keyways.

The drawing is further simplified by giving the keyway dimensions in the legend instead of dimensioning the drawing.

Ques. What should be noted about the arrangement of the drawings in figs. 10 to 12?

Ans. The two sections are placed on the right side of the full view drawing instead of being "strung" on the XX axis where they really belong.

Ques. Is this admissible and good practice?

Ans. Yes, when it is expedient to make a special arrangement of the views.

In the first place all the dimensions are vertical in which position they are easily read; moreover the blue print is easily handled as compared with a longer drawing.

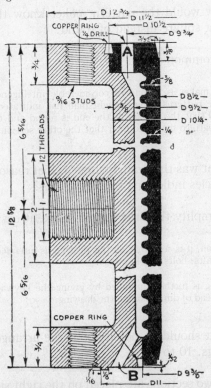

FIG. 13.—Half sectional view elevation of Graham jacketed cylinder showing cylinder wall, liner inlet and outlet ports and other details showing especially complete representation with only *a half cross sectional view.*

Sections and Sectional Views.—These are necessary in many drawings to bring out and fully dimension the object. Usually one section or sectional view is sufficient, but for some irregular objects several may be required.

Frequently one sectional view is used in place of a full view and a section.

Sometimes an object is of such symmetrical outline it can be completely shown with one cross section, and in fact with only one half of the cross section.

An example of showing complete representation with only a half cross sectional view is the jacketed engine cylinder designed by the author, as shown in fig. 13.

This drawing illustrates several things. First, all the horizontal dimensions are marked D, which means *diameter*. Some of these D, horizontal dimensions are continued in line with separate dimensions as ⅜ thickness of cylinder wall, ¼ minimum thickness of liner, etc. About the only thing not indicated is number of jacket outlet passages at **A** and **B**. However, a legend could be added giving number of air passages and number of studs.

Ques. Mention something open to criticism on this drawing.

Ans. The method of making fractions in putting on the dimensions.

As before stated the division line of a fraction should be horizontal instead of inclined. However, on this particular drawing the fractions are made with such care that there is no possibility of making any mistake.

Sections for Irregular Objects.—Some objects owing to their shape require more than one section for complete showing. For instance, figs. 14 to 16 is an example in which two sectional views are necessary. As an aid to blue print reading, the various views should be labeled, as in this case: bottom plan, section on **AB**, section on **CD**, which leaves nothing to the imagination.

With all dimensions put on, the views become a *working drawing* from which the machinist gets all information to machine the object, which is a combined lower cylinder head and entablature, used with some types of engine.

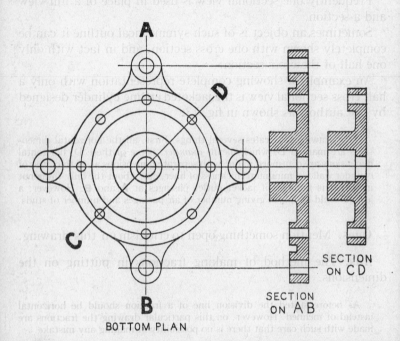

Figs. 14 to 16.—Views of engine combined lower cylinder head and entablature illustrating object requiring a full view and two sections.

Ribs in Plane of Section.—On some objects such as pulleys having radial ribs or spokes, in order to show the shape of the latter as well as the rim, it is necessary to take a section on a plane through the arm.

When a rib comes on the plane of a section it is desirable to distinguish between the section and the rib.

Ques. How is the distinction made?

Ans. By using fine section lines for the section and coarse lines for the rib, as in fig. 18.

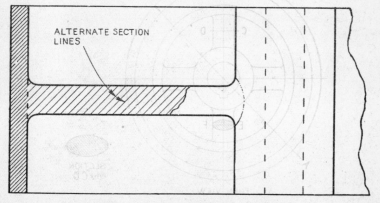

ALTERNATE SECTION LINES

FIGS. 17 and 18.—Drawings of a pulley illustrating *fine and coarse section lining*, on sections with ribs in plane of section.

Ques. What is the practical method of drawing the section lines?

Ans. By omitting alternate lines on the rib section.

This method gives a pleasing appearance to the drawing and the dotted contour lines indicate clearly the shape and thickness of the rim section.

Ques. How may this alternate sectioning be avoided?

Ans. By taking a section on a plane between ribs and showing a separate or detail cross section of the ribs.

Thus in figs. 19 to 21, first the full view of the wheel is drawn and then the sectional view taken on AB midway between the ribs; this eliminates having the rib section joined onto the section of the rim and gives a better idea of the wheel. The cross shape of the ribs is clearly shown by the section taken on CD, fig. 20. Note that the three views are each labeled as should be for quick and easy blue print reading.

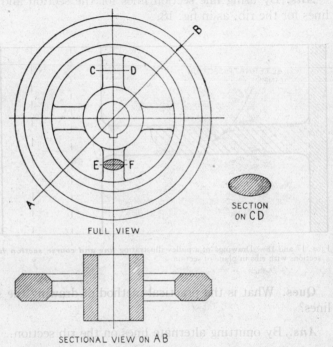

FULL VIEW

SECTION
ON CD

SECTIONAL VIEW ON AB

FIGS. 19 to 21.—Plan and elevation of Shipman fly wheel.

Ques. What would be a better location for the section on **CD**?

Ans. Instead of making a separate drawing, place it across one of the arms as at EF in the full view drawing fig. 19.

Ques. What help is this in blue print reading?

Ans. The mechanic after looking at the separate sectional view does not have to locate CD in the full view, but when the section is placed across the arms as at EF, the location of the section is at once seen.

Ques. How should the principal dimensions (diameters) be put on the fly wheel?

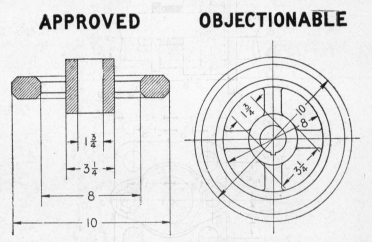

Figs. 22 and 23.—Approved and objectionable methods of dimensioning the Shipman fly wheel shown in figs. 19 to 21.

Ans. On the sectional view rather than the full view.

Ques. Why?

Ans. To avoid dimensions at various angles and crowding.

Evidently when placed as in fig. 22 they are easily read; fig. 23 shows objectionable arrangement, the effect being virtually a "mess of dimensions."

Objects Suitable for Sectional Views.—Some machine details are specially adapted for representation by sectional views, such as drawings of objects which include bolts, studs, pistons, piston rods and other cylindrical parts.

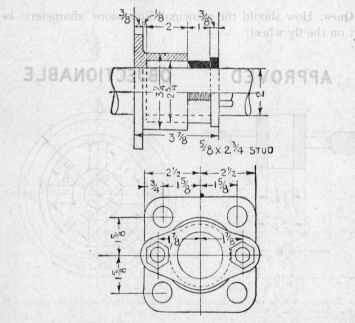

FIGS. 24 and 25.—Inside marine stuffing box as designed by the author for the yacht "Stornaway II."

The sectional view compared with a section is more pictorial, shows up the object more plainly and saves time in drawing. A typical object for a sectional view is the familiar stuffing box.

As an example of this, figs. 24 and 25 show a marine stuffing box for the propeller shaft of a small boat. It is fully shown by a sectional view and right end elevation. Considering the sectional view, fig. 24, the center line divides the drawing into a half full view (below center line) and a sectional view proper above the center line. Here the upper half of the stuffing box and gland is in section, the box being section lined and the packing gland in solid black.

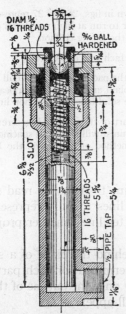
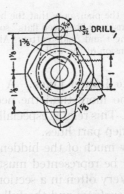

FIGS. 26 and 27.—Spring cushion feed pump. The author, who had many years' experience designing large pumps for city water works found that the so-called air chambers were virtually water chambers, because unless means were provided to keep them filled with air, they soon became filled with water and ceased to perform their function of cushioning the shocks. Accordingly such device is here dispensed with, and a spring cushion provided which is expected to absorb the shocks even at high speed. No valves are built into the pump casting, a tee fitting and two check valves being used, connected with close nipples.

The occasional use of solid black instead of section lines makes a drawing snappy and easier to read.

Evidently the box and gland are better defined than if both were section lined.

Ques. On a sectional view such as in fig. 24 what is some-times done to make the drawing more pictorial?

Ans. The cylindrical parts are shaded.

An example of such treatment is shown in figs. 26 and 27 representing a special feed pump designed by the author to run at high speed and pressure without hammer or water knock due to the spring cushion.

Note shading on the plunger part of which is in cross section.

The stuffing box is of the screw type, the packing gland and ball retainer being in solid black section. Note how plain and sharp they appear in the drawing due to the contrast between the solid black and section lines.

In the plan, note that the hexagon part of the stuffing box screw cap is dimensioned "between flats" so the machinist will know the spacing for the milling r and l side cutters. Also note method of putting on the $1\frac{3}{8}$ inch dimension of the well.

As to Dotted Lines.—A blue print to be easily read should have no more than the necessary lines to fully represent the object. This relates especially to dotted lines whether projection or hidden part lines.

How much of the hidden part behind the plane of a section should be represented must be determined for each particular case. Very often in a sectional view only the outline of the sectional surfaces and the full lines will appear.

Except in special cases this is all that is necessary and filling up the drawing with dotted lines will only make it harder to read and more difficult for the draughtsman to find room for the dimensions.

Detail Drawings.—There are two kinds of working drawings:

1. Assembly drawings
2. Detail drawings

Ques. What is an assembly drawing?

Ans. A drawing of a multi-part object showing it as a whole, that is, all its parts assembled in their proper positions.

Ques. What is the object of a multi-part object?

Ans. It shows the mechanic how to put together the various parts which make up the object.

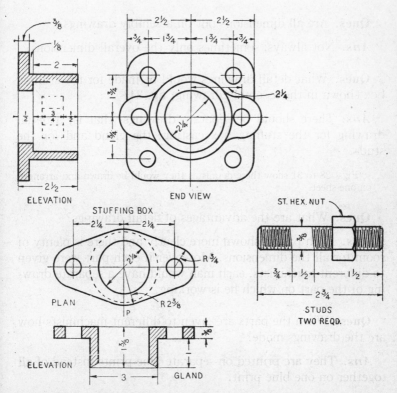

Figs. 28 to 31.—Detail drawings for the marine stuffing box shown in the assembly drawing, figs. 24 and 25.

Ques. What is important on an assembly drawing and why?

Ans. Complete overall dimensions to indicate how much space will be required in installation.

Ques. What drawings in this chapter are assembly drawings?

Ans. Figs. 2, 13, 22 and 30.

Ques. Are all dimensions put on assembly drawings?

Ans. Not always; sometimes only the overall dimensions.

Ques. What detail drawings would be made for the stuffing box shown in the assembly drawing, fig. 24?

Ans. There should be separate drawings, that is, a detail drawing for the stuffing box casting, the gland and for the studs.

Figs. 28 to 31 show these details as they would be drawn and arranged on one sheet.

Ques. What are the advantages of detail drawings?

Ans. Each part is shown more clearly and there is plenty of room for all the dimensions. Moreover if each part were given to different machinists, each man would have a separate drawing of the part on which he is working.

Ques. When the parts are given to different machinists how are the drawings made?

Ans. They are printed on separate blue prints instead of all together on one blue print.

CHAPTER 9

ASA
Z32.

Proposed Revision

American Standard

GRAPHICAL SYMBOLS

For Use on Drawings
IN MECHANICAL ENGINEERING

American Standards Association

SPONSOR ORGANIZATIONS
American Institute of Electrical Engineers
The American Society of Mechanical Engineers
29 West 39th Street, New York, N. Y.

December, 1940

WITH the organization of the Sectional Committee on Standards for Drawings and Drafting Room Practice in 1926 six subcommittees were appointed to develop the various phases of this project. To Subcommittee No. 6 was assigned the development of a set of standard graphical symbols for use on drawings. At its December, 1928, meeting the committee reviewed a number of suggested series of symbols including (1) those proposed by the American Society of Heating and Ventilating *Engineers in 1925 and (2) those proposed in 1926 by the National Association of Master Plumbers of the United States, and approved in revised form in 1929.

In the preparation of the tentative proposal the committee drew on material from the publications of various organizations. Copies of this draft were distributed broadly to industry for criticism and comment in July, 1932. After a thorough study the subcommittee made its report to the Sectional Committee. Upon approval by this committee the standard was submitted for approval to the sponsor bodies and the American Standards Association. It received the designation of American Standard in November, 1935, with the serial number Z14.2-1935.

During the last stages of this activity a number of interested groups including the ASA Electrical Standards Committee requested that this project be broadened. Accordingly, in November, 1933, the American Standards Association called a conference to which were invited representatives of the sponsors of the Sectional Committee on Standardization of Letter Symbols and Abbreviations for Science and Engineering (Z10) and the Sectional Committee on Standards for Drawings and Drafting Room Practice (Z14), respectively, together with officers of these sectional committees and of the E.S.C. Committee on Scopes, the technical advisers to the U. S. National Committee of the International Electrotechnical Commission on Letter Symbols, and certain interested individuals.

After a frank discussion of the activities of Sectional Committees Z10 and Z14 and the desired further development of the subject of graphical symbols and abbreviations for use on drawings, it was agreed that all of the activity on graphical symbols should be concentrated in a new sectional committee sponsored by the American Institute of Electrical Engineers and The American Society of Mechanical Engineers, the committee to be known as Z32 on Standardization of Graphical Symbols and Abbreviations for Use on Drawings. It was further agreed that the projects on graphical symbols so far completed or in progress by Sectional Committees Z10 and Z14 should be transferred to Z32 after the present plans for publication had been consummated.

These agreements were transmitted to the sponsor societies of the two committees in January, 1934. Their approval was given and the recommendations were passed on to the ASA which authorized this realignment in June, 1935.

At the organization meeting held in June, 1936, the work was divided between two subcommittees—Subcommittee No. 1 covering Symbols in Mechanical Engineering, and Subcommittee No. 2 covering Symbols in Electrical Engineering.

To bring the existing standard in line with the best current practice, a revision of Z14.2-1935 was begun by Subcommittee No. 1 and its subgroups providing for the addition of symbols on air-conditioning, sprinklers, pneumatic tubes, ductwork, refrigerating, and welding. The welding symbols included in this standard were developed by the Symbols Committee of the American Welding Society, and the refrigerating symbols by a similar committee of the Air Conditioning and Refrigerating Machinery Association.

A preliminary draft of the new material was first presented to the members of the sectional committee at a meeting held in December, 1939. Slight changes in the welding symbols and the footnotes applying to them were made subsequent to that meeting. The revised proposal now known as Z 32. was approved by letter ballot vote of the sectional committee, and, following approval by the sponsor bodies, was presented to the American Standards Association with recommendation for approval as an American Standard. This designation was given in........

Officers of Sectional Committee
Standardization of Graphical Symbols and Abbreviations
for Use on Drawings

H. W. Samson, *Chairman*   W. L. Heard, *Secretary*

T. E. French, *Chairman*, Subcommittee No. 1 on Symbols for Use in Mechanical Engineering

L. C. Bibber, *Chairman*, Subgroup No. 1 on Graphical Symbols for Welding

E. E. Ashley, *Chairman*, Subgroup No. 2 on Graphical Symbols for Heating, Ventilation, Refrigeration, and Air Conditioning

Published by
The American Society of Mechanical Engineers, 29 West 39th Street, New York, N. Y.

December, 1940

Graphical Symbols for Use on Drawings

Plumbing

1 Corner Bath

2 Recessed Bath

3 Roll Rim Bath

4 Sitz Bath

SB

5 Foot Bath

FB

6 Bidet

B

7 Shower Stall

8 Shower Head

(Plan) (Elev.)

9 Overhead Gang Shower

(Plan)

(Elev.)

10 Pedestal Lavatory

PL

11 Wall Lavatory

WL

12 Corner Lavatory

LAV

13 Manicure Lavatory Medical Lavatory

ML

14 Dental Lavatory

DENTAL LAV

15 Plain Kitchen Sink

S

16 Kitchen Sink R & L Drain Board

Graphical Symbols for Use on Drawings		*Plumbing*

17	Kitchen Sink L. H. Drain Board	
18	Combination Sink and Dishwasher	
19	Combination Sink and Laundry Tray	S & T
20	Service Sink	SS
21	Wash Sink (Wall Type)	
22	Wash Sink	
23	Laundry Tray	L T
24	Water Closet (Low Tank)	

25	Water Closet (No Tank)	
26	Urinal (Pedestal Type)	
27	Urinal (Wall Type)	
28	Urinal (Corner Type)	
29	Urinal (Stall Type)	
30	Urinal (Trough Type)	TU
31	Drinking Fountain (Pedestal Type)	DF
32	Drinking Fountain (Wall Type)	DF

Graphical Symbols for Use on Drawings

Plumbing

33 Drinking Fountain
(Trough Type)

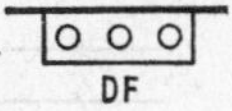

| o | o | o |
DF

34 Hot Water Tank

HW
T

35 Water Heater

WH

36 Meter

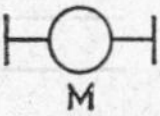

M

37 Hose Rack

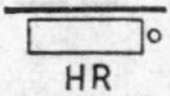

HR

38 Hose Bib

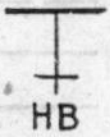

HB

39 Gas Outlet

G

40 Vacuum Outlet

41 Drain

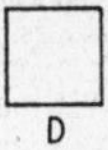

D

42 Grease Separator

G

43 Oil Separator

O

44 Cleanout

C
O

45 Garage Drain

o

46 Floor Drain With
Backwater Valve

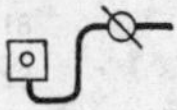

o

47 Roof Sump

Graphical Symbols
for Use on Drawings

Piping

HEATING

60	High Pressure Steam	
61	Medium Pressure Steam	
62	Low Pressure Steam	
63	High Pressure Return	
64	Medium Pressure Return	
65	Low Pressure Return	
66	Boiler Blow Off	
67	Condensate or Vacuum Pump Discharge	
68	Feedwater Pump Discharge	
69	Make Up Water	
70	Air Relief Line	
71	Fuel Oil Flow	F O F
72	Fuel Oil Return	F O R
73	Fuel Oil Tank Vent	F O V
74	Compressed Air	A
75	Hot Water Heating Supply	
76	Hot Water Heating Return	

AIR CONDITIONING

80	Refrigerant Discharge	R D
81	Refrigerant Suction	R S
82	Condenser Water Flow	C
83	Condenser Water Return	C R
84	Circulating Chilled or Hot Water Flow	C H
85	Circulating Chilled or Hot Water Return	C H R
86	Make Up Water	
87	Humidification Line	H
88	Drain	D
89	Brine Supply	B
90	Brine Return	B R

Graphical Symbols
  for Use on Drawings

Piping

PLUMBING

100 Soil, Waste or Leader (Above Grade)

101 Soil, Waste or Leader (Below Grade)

102 Vent

103 Cold Water

104 Hot Water

105 Hot Water Return

106 Fire Line —F— —F—

107 Gas —G— —G—

108 Acid Waste ACID

109 Drinking Water Flow

110 Drinking Water Return

111 Vacuum Cleaning —V— —V—

112 Compressed Air —A—

SPRINKLERS

120 Main Supplies —S—

121 Branch and Head —o— —o—

122 Drain —S— —S—

PNEUMATIC TUBES

123 Tube Runs

Graphical Symbols for Use on Drawings	Flanged	Screwed	Bell and Spigot	Welded	Soldered
130 Join					
131 Elbow—90 deg					
132 Elbow—45 deg					
133 Elbow—Turned Up					
134 Elbow—Turned Down					
135 Elbow—Long Radius					
136 Side Outlet Elbow—Outlet Down					
137 Side Outlet Elbow—Outlet Up					
138 Base Elbow					
139 Double Branch Elbow					

Pipe Fittings and Valves

Graphical Symbols for Use on Drawings

Pipe Fittings and Valves

	Flanged	Screwed	Bell and Spigot	Welded	Soldered
140 Single Sweep Tee					
141 Double Sweep Tee					
142 Reducing Elbow					
143 Tee					
144 Tee—Outlet Up					
145 Tee—Outlet Down					
146 Side Outlet Tee Outlet Up					
147 Side Outlet Tee Outlet Down					
148 Cross					
149 Reducer					

Graphical Symbols for Use on Drawings					
Pipe Fittings and Valves	Flanged	Screwed	Bell and Spigot	Welded	Soldered
150 Eccentric Reducer					
151 Lateral					
152 Gate Valve					
153 Globe Valve					
154 Angle Globe Valve					
155 Angle Gate Valve					
156 Check Valve					
157 Angle Check Valve					
158 Stop Cock					
159 Safety Valve					

Graphical Symbols for Use on Drawings				*Pipe Fittings and Valves*	
	Flanged	Screwed	Bell and Spigot	Welded	Soldered
160 Quick Opening Valve					
161 Float Operating Valve					
162 Motor Operated Gate Valve					
Motor Operated Globe Valve					
163 Expansion Joint Flanged					
164 Reducing Flange					
165 Union	(See No. 130)				
166 Sleeve					
167 Bushing					

Graphical Symbols for Use on Drawings

Heating and Ventilating

170 Heat Transfer Surface, Plan	
171 Wall Radiator, Plan	
172 Wall Radiator on Ceiling, Plan	
173 Unit Heater (Propeller), Plan	
174 Unit Heater (Centrifugal Fan), Plan	
175 Unit Ventilator, Plan	

TRAPS

176 Thermostatic	
177 Blast Thermostatic	
178 Float and Thermostatic	
179 Float	
180 Boiler Return	

VALVES

181 Reducing Pressure	
182 Air Line	
183 Lock and Shield	
184 Diaphragm	
185 Air Eliminator	
186 Strainer	
187 Thermometer	
188 Thermostat	

Graphical Symbols
for Use on Drawings
Ductwork

200 Duct (1st Figure, Width; 2nd, Depth)		12 × 20
201 Direction of Flow		→
202 Inclined Drop in Respect to Air Flow		D
203 Inclined Rise in Respect to Air Flow		R
204 Supply Duct Section		← 12 × 20
205 Exhaust Duct Section	E	← 12 × 20
206 Recirculation Duct Section	R	← 12 × 20
207 Fresh Air Duct Section	F A	← 12 × 20
208 Other Ducts Section	K E	(Label) Kitchen Exh.
209 Register		R
210 Grille		G
211 Supply Outlet		‖ →
212 Exhaust Inlet		‖ ←
213 Top Register or Grille		TR 20×12 – 700 cfm / TG 20×12 – 700 cfm
214 Center Register or Grille		CR 20×12 – 700 cfm / CG 20×12 – 700 cfm
215 Bottom Register or Grille		BR 20×12 – 700 cfm / BG 20×12 – 700 cfm
216 Top and Bottom Register or Grille		T&BR 20×12 – ea. 700 cfm / T&BG 20×12 – ea. 700 cfm
217 Ceiling Register or Grille		CK 20×12 – 700 cfm / CG 20×12 – 700 cfm
218 Louver Opening		L 20×12 – 700 cfm
219 Adjustable Plaque		P – 20×12 – 700 cfm / P – 20"φ – 700 cfm

Graphical Symbols for Use on Drawings

Ductwork

220 Volume Damper

221 Deflecting Damper

222 Deflecting Damper, Up

223 Deflecting Damper, Down

224 Adjustable Blank Off

225 Vanes

226 Automatic Dampers

227 Canvas Connections

228 Fan and Motor With Belt Guard

229 Intake Louvers and Screen

Graphical Symbols for Use on Drawings

Heat-Power Apparatus

240 Steam Generator
   (Boiler)

241 Flue Gas Reheater
   (Intermediate Superheater)

242 Live Steam Superheater

243 Feed Heater With
   Air Outlet

244 Steam Turbine

245 Surface Condenser

246 Condensing Turbine

247 Open Tank

248 Closed Tank

249 Automatic
   Reducing Valve

250 Automatic
   By-pass Valve

251 Automatic Valve
   Operated by Governor

252 Pumps
   Boiler Feed
   Service
   Condensate
   Circulating Water
   Air

   Reciprocating

253 Dynamic Pump
   (Air Ejector)

Graphical Symbols for Use on Drawings

Conventional Rivets

260 Shop Rivets, Two Full Heads

261 Shop Rivets, Countersunk and Chipped, Near Side

262 Shop Rivets, Countersunk and Chipped, Far Side

263 Shop Rivets, Countersunk and Chipped, Both Sides

264 Shop Rivets, Countersunk but Not Chipped, Max. ⅛ in. High   Near Side

265 Shop Rivets, Countersunk but Not Chipped, Max. ⅛ in. High   Far Side

266 Shop Rivets, Countersunk but Not Chipped, Max. ⅛ in. High   Both Sides

267 Shop Rivets, Flattened to ¼ in. High for ½ in. and ⅝ in. Rivets   Near Side

268 Shop Rivets, Flattened to ¼ in. High for ½ in. and ⅝ in. Rivets   Far Side

269 Shop Rivets, Flattened to ¼ in. High for ½ in. and ⅝ in. Rivets   Both Sides

270 Shop Rivets, Flattened to ⅜ in. High for ¾, ⅞, and 1 in. Rivets   Near Side

271 Shop Rivets, Flattened to ⅜ in. High for ¾, ⅞, and 1 in. Rivets   Far Side

272 Shop Rivets, Flattened to ⅜ in. High for ¾, ⅞, and 1 in. Rivets   Both Sides

273 Field Rivets, Two Full Heads

274 Field Rivets, Countersunk and Chipped, Near Side

275 Field Rivets, Countersunk and Chipped, Far Side

276 Field Rivets, Countersunk and Chipped, Both Sides

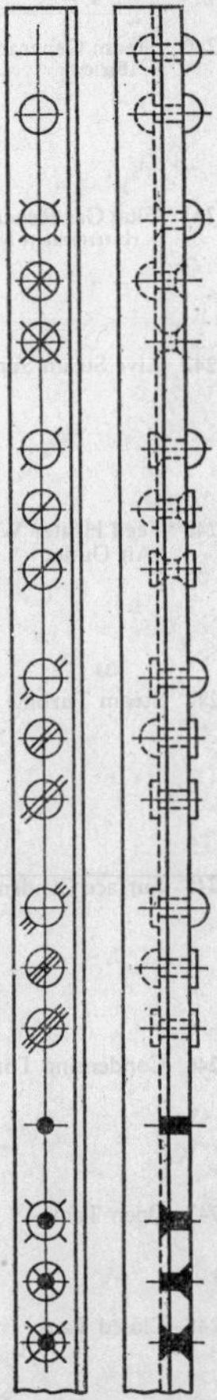

Graphical Symbols
for Use on Drawings

Refrigerating

280 Thermostat
   (Self Contained)

281 Thermostat
   (Remote Bulb)

282 Pressurestat

283 Hand Expansion Valve

284 Automatic
   Expansion Valve

285 Thermostatic
   Expansion Valve

EVAPORATOR PRESS

   286 Regulating Valve,
      Throttling Type
      (Evaporator Side)

   287 Regulating Valve,
      Thermostatic
      Throttling Type

   288 Regulating Valve,
      Snap-Action Valve

289 Compressor Suction
   Pressure Limiting
   Valve, Throttling Type
   (Compressor Side)

290 Hand Shut Off Valve

291 Thermal Bulb

292 Scale Trap

293 Dryer

294 Strainer

295 High Side Float

296 Low Side Float

297 Gage

298 Finned Type Cooling Unit,
   Natural Convection

299 Pipe Coil

300 Forced Convection
   Cooling Unit

301 Immersion Cooling Unit

302 Ice Making Unit

303 Heat Interchanger

304 Condensing Unit,
   Air Cooled

305 Condensing Unit,
   Water Cooled

Graphical Symbols for Use on Drawings

Refrigerating

306 Compressor

307 Cooling Tower

308 Evaporative Condenser

309 Solenoid Valve

310 Pressurestat With High Pressure Cut-Out

APPENDIX

Graphical Symbols for Use on Drawings	*Welding*

ARC AND GAS WELDING

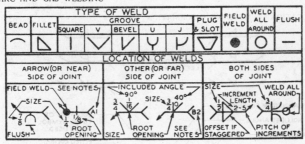

The side of the joint to which the arrow points is the arrow (or near) side.

Both-sides welds of same type are of same size unless otherwise shown.

Symbols apply between abrupt changes in direction of joint or as dimensioned (except where all around symbol is used).

All welds are continuous and of user's standard proportions, unless otherwise shown.

Tail of arrow used for specification reference (tail may be omitted when reference is not used).

Dimensions of weld sizes, increment lengths and spacings are given in inches.

RESISTANCE WELDING

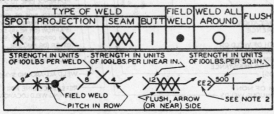

Symbols apply between abrupt changes in direction of joint, or as dimensioned (except where all around symbol is used).

Tail or arrow used for specification reference (tail may be omitted when reference is not used).

All spacings are given in inches.

NOTE: Further information on the use of these symbols will be found in "Welding Symbols and Instructions for Their Use," published by the American Welding Society, New York, N. Y., price 25 cents.

Graphical Symbols for Use on Drawings

Welding

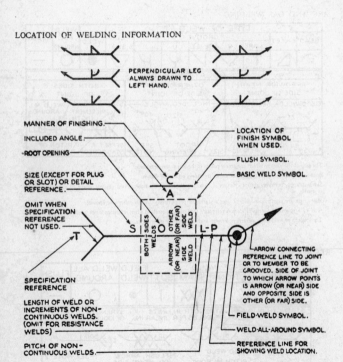

LOCATION OF WELDING INFORMATION

PERPENDICULAR LEG ALWAYS DRAWN TO LEFT HAND.

MANNER OF FINISHING.

INCLUDED ANGLE.

ROOT OPENING

SIZE (EXCEPT FOR PLUG OR SLOT) OR DETAIL REFERENCE.

OMIT WHEN SPECIFICATION REFERENCE NOT USED.

SPECIFICATION REFERENCE

LENGTH OF WELD OR INCREMENTS OF NON-CONTINUOUS WELDS. (OMIT FOR RESISTANCE WELDS)

PITCH OF NON-CONTINUOUS WELDS.

LOCATION OF FINISH SYMBOL WHEN USED.

FLUSH SYMBOL.

BASIC WELD SYMBOL.

BOTH SIDES WELDS

OTHER (OR FAR) SIDE WELD

ARROW (OR NEAR) SIDE WELD

ARROW CONNECTING REFERENCE LINE TO JOINT OR TO MEMBER TO BE GROOVED. SIDE OF JOINT TO WHICH ARROW POINTS IS ARROW (OR NEAR) SIDE AND OPPOSITE SIDE IS OTHER (OR FAR) SIDE.

FIELD-WELD SYMBOL.

WELD-ALL-AROUND SYMBOL.

REFERENCE LINE FOR SHOWING WELD LOCATION.

NOTE Further information on the use of these symbols will be found in "Welding Symbols and Instructions for Their Use," published by the American Welding Society, New York, N. Y., price 25 cents.

APPENDIX—*Electric Power and Wiring*[1]

	One Line	Complete [2]		One Line	Complete [2]
A-C Generator or Motor— Basic Symbol [3]			Air Circuit Breaker		
D-C Generator or Motor— Basic Symbol			Fuse		
Induction Motor [3]			Resistor		
Synchronous Converter [3]			Rheostat		
			Reactor		
Direct Connected Units— Basic Symbols [3]			Capacitor [4]		
Single-Phase Two-Winding Transformer—Basic Symbols [3,4]			Lightning Arrestor Basic Symbol [4]		
Disconnecting Switch Basic Symbol			Indicating Instrument— Basic Symbol [5]	(I)	(6)
Knife Switch, Single-Throw			Graphic Instrument Basic Symbol	◯ GRAPH	(6)
Double-Throw Switch			Ampere-Hour Meter	(AH)	(6)
			Ammeter	(A)	(6)
Oil Circuit Breaker, Single-Throw			Frequency Meter	(F)	(6)
			Watthour Meter	(WH)	(6)

APPENDIX—*Electric Power and Wiring*[1]

	One Line	Complete [2]		One Line	Complete [2]
Wattmeter	(W)	(6)	Conductors, Crossing but not Connected		
Voltmeter	(V)	(6)	Conductors, Crossing and Electrically Connected		
Instrument Shunt			Conductors (with Branches)		
Conductors			Bus (with Branches)		
			Ground Connection		

[1] These Symbols for Electric Power and Wiring were selected from the American Standard for Graphical Symbols used for Electric Power and Wiring ASA Z10g2-1933.

[2] The "complete" symbol is intended to illustrate the method of treatment for any desired polyphase combination rather than to show the exact symbol required.

[3] Use symbol (~\/\/\/\/\~) for windings of apparatus as required, and connect to suit particular case. It is recognized that no symbol list can show symbols for complete diagrams for all possible methods of connection.

[4] This symbol has not been approved as American Standard because there is still a major difference of opinion concerning the representation of this piece of equipment.

[5] Letter within circle indicates type of instrument if but one is used. If more than one instrument is used, "I" appears within the circle with abbreviation alongside.

(6) For complete symbol show outline approximating that of rear view of actual device and indicate terminals in actual relative location, current terminals by open circles and potential terminals by solid circles. Scale range and type number may be marked adjacent to symbol, if desired.

CHAPTER 10

American Standards for

Graphical Electrical Symbols

for

Architectural Plans

(Revision of C10-1924—A.I.E.E. No. 42)

American Standards Association
Approved February 6. 1943

SPONSORS

American Institute of Electrical Engineers
American Society of Mechanical Engineers.

Published by
American Institute of Electrical Engineers
33 West Thirty-ninth Street, New York

Foreword

GRAPHICAL ELECTRICAL SYMBOLS FOR ARCHITECTURAL PLANS — Z32.9

HISTORY

In 1921 a conference of bodies interested in symbols for electrical equipment of buildings was called at the suggestion of the American Institute of Architects and the National Electrical Contractors Association. A tentative American Standard, C10, was approved in 1924 with the AIA, the NECA and the AIEE as sponsors. In 1936 the three original sponsors agreed to the transfer of the work of C10 to sectional Committee Z32 "Standardization of Graphical Symbols and Abbreviations for Use on Drawings" under the sponsorship of ASME and AIEE.

SCOPE

This standard, which has the endorsement of the American Institute of Architects is intended to cover the symbols used for depicting electrical equipment for buildings and are the schematics used by the architectural profession to show the locations of electrical power, light, control and communication facilities provided for the building. These symbols have been made as simple as possible and are not intended in any way to depict the structure of the particular devices shown.

SYMBOL SIZE

It is not the intention of this standard to set the size of the particular conventions as used on the drawing. These should be drawn to a size commensurate with the particular drawing being made.

The size of wire or conduit is not to be designated or implied by the symbol, although the following factors are: (1) number of wires in a conduit, (2) use (branch circuit, feeder, auxiliary system) and (3) location (ceiling, floor)

MODIFICATION

The symbols can be modified by upper case letters and other distinguishing marks placed in the center, and by subscript letters or numbers placed at the lower right. Upper case letters used as subscripts shall refer to standard types; numerals shall refer to standard numerical variations; lower case letters shall have a meaning, varying with each drawing or set of drawings, but explained in the key of symbols accompanying the drawings.

Officers of Sectional Committee Z32
STANDARDIZATION OF GRAPHICAL SYMBOLS AND ABBREVIATIONS
FOR USE ON DRAWINGS

H. W. Samson. *Chairman*   W. L. Heard, *Secretary*

SUBGROUP No. 6 ARCHITECTURAL SYMBOLS

E. A. Brand, *Chairman*   R. G. Slauer, *Secretary*

E. C. Alger	F. R. Fowler	W. G. Hill
T. I. Coe	J. R. Gramm	L. C. Horle
A. Coggeshall	H. F. Harvey	R. B. Shepard
J. C. Forsyth		E. C. Stanton

GENERAL OUTLETS

Ceiling / Wall

Ceiling	Wall	
O	O	Outlet.
B	B	Blanked Outlet.
D		Drop Cord.
E	E	Electrical Outlet; for use only when circle alone might be confused with columns, plumbing symbols, etc.
F	F	Fan Outlet.
J	J	Junction Box.
L	L	Lamp Holder.
L_PS	L_PS	Lamp Holder with Pull Switch.
S	S	Pull Switch.
V	V	Outlet for Vapor Discharge Lamp.
X	X	Exit Light Outlet.
C	C	Clock Outlet. (Specify Voltage)

CONVENIENCE OUTLETS

Duplex Convenience Outlet.

Convenience Outlet other than Duplex. 1 = Single, 3 = Triplex, etc.

Weatherproof Convenience Outlet.

Range Outlet.

Switch and Convenience Outlet.

Radio and Convenience Outlet.

Special Purpose Outlet. (Des. in Spec.)

Floor Outlet.

SWITCH OUTLETS

S	Single Pole Switch.
S₂	Double Pole Switch.
S₃	Three Way Switch.
S₄	Four Way Switch.
S_D	Automatic Door Switch.
S_E	Electrolier Switch.
S_K	Key Operated Switch.
S_P	Switch and Pilot Lamp.
S_CB	Circuit Breaker.
S_WCB	Weatherproof Circuit Breaker.
S_MC	Momentary Contact Switch.
S_RC	Remote Control Switch.
S_WP	Weatherproof Switch.
S_F	Fused Switch.
S_WF	Weatherproof Fused Switch.

SPECIAL OUTLETS

O_a,b,c,etc / _a,b,c,etc / S_a,b,c,etc

Any Standard Symbol as given above with the addition of a lower case subscript letter may be used to designate some special variation of Standard Equipment of particular interest in a specific set of Architectural Plans.

When used they must be listed in the Key of Symbols on each drawing and if necessary further described in the specifications.

PANELS, CIRCUITS, AND MISCELLANEOUS

Lighting Panel.

Power Panel.

— Branch Circuit; Concealed in Ceiling or Wall.

--- Branch Circuit; Concealed in Floor.

----- Branch Circuit; Exposed.

Home Run to Panel Board. Indicate number of Circuits by number of arrows.
Note: Any circuit without further designation indicates a two-wire circuit. For a greater number of wires indicate as follows: —///— (3 wires) —////— (4 wires), etc.

Feeders. Note: Use heavy lines and designate by number corresponding to listing in Feeder Schedule.

Underfloor Duct and Junction Box. Triple System.
Note: For double or single systems eliminate one or two lines. This symbol is equally adaptable to auxiliary system layouts.

G	Generator.
M	Motor.
I	Instrument.
T	Power Transformer. (Or draw to scale.)
	Controller.
	Isolating Switch.

AUXILIARY SYSTEMS

•	Push Button.
	Buzzer.
	Bell.
◇	Annunciator.
	Outside Telephone.
	Interconnecting Telephone.
	Telephone Switchboard.
T	Bell Ringing Transformer.
D	Electric Door Opener.
F	Fire Alarm Bell.
F	Fire Alarm Station.
X	City Fire Alarm Station.
FA	Fire Alarm Central Station.
FS	Automatic Fire Alarm Device.
W	Watchman's Station.
W	Watchman's Central Station.
H	Horn.
N	Nurse's Signal Plug.
M	Maid's Signal Plug.
R	Radio Outlet.
SC	Signal Central Station.
	Interconnection Box.
	Battery.

----- Auxiliary System Circuits.
Note: Any line without further designation indicates a 2-Wire System. For a greater number of wires designate with numerals in manner similar to ----12-No. 18W-3/4" C., or designate by number corresponding to listing in Schedule.

_a,b,c Special Auxiliary Outlets.
Subscript letters refer to notes on plans or detailed description in specifications.

Allowable Carrying Capacities of Wires

(According to the National Electrical Code)

Gage No.	Diameter of Solid Wires in Mils	Area in Circular Mils	Column A Rubber Insulation Amperes	Column B Varnished Cambric Insulation, Amperes	Column C Other Insulation Amperes
18	40.3	1,624	3		5
16	50.8	2,583	6		10
14	64.1	4,107	15	18	20
12	80.8	6,530	20	25	25
10	101.9	10,380	25	30	30
8	128.5	16,510	35	40	50
6	162.0	26,250	50	60	70
5	181.9	33,100	55	65	80
4	204.3	41,740	70	85	90
3	229.4	52,630	80	95	100
2	257.6	66,370	90	110	125
1	289.3	83,690	100	120	150
0	325.	105,500	125	150	200
00	364.8	133,100	150	180	225
000	409.6	167,800	175	210	275
0000	460.	200,000	200	240	325
		211,600	225	270	360
		250,000	250	300	400
		300,000	275	330	450
		350,000	300	360	500
		400,000	325	390	550
		500,000	400	480	600
		600,000	450	540	680
		700,000	500	600	760
		800,000	550	660	840
		900,000	600	720	920
		1,000,000	660	780	1,000
		1,100,000	690	830	1,080
		1,200,000	730	880	1,150
		1,300,000	770	920	1,220
		1,400,000	810	970	1,290
		1,500,000	850	1,020	1,360
		1,600,000	890	1,070	1,430
		1,700,000	930	1,120	1,490
		1,800,000	970	1,160-	1,550
		1,900,000	1,010	1,210	1,610
		2,000,000	1,050	1,260	1,610

1 Mil = 0.001 inch.

Standardized Stranding

(According to the National Electrical Code)

Strands No. of Strands	Mils Dia.	Gage No.	Cable Area in Cir. Mils	Outside Dia. over Copper	Column A Rubber Insulation	Column B Varnished Cambric Insulation	Column C Other Insulation
7/	25	22	4,490	.075	15	18	20
7/	32	20	7,150	.096	20	25	25
7/	40	18	11,370	.120	25	30	35
7/	51	16	18,080	.153	35	40	50
7/	64	14	28,740	.192	50	60	70
7/	81	12	45,710	.253	70	85	90
7/	91	11	58,000	.273	80	95	110
7/	102	10	72,680	.306	90	110	130
19/	64	14	78,030	.320	100	120	150
19/	72	13	98,880	.360	125	150	175
19/	81	12	124,900	.405	150	180	210
19/	91	11	157,300	.455	175	210	250
19/	107	11*	217,500	.540	225	270	325
19/	114	9	248,700	.570	250	300	350
37/	91	11	306,400	.687	275	330	400
37/	97	10*	347,500	.679	300	360	450
37/	102	10	381,200	.714	325	390	500
37/	116	9*	494,500	.798	400	480	600
61/	107	10*	633,300	.918	475	565	700
61/	102	9	698,000	.963	500	600	750
61/	114	9*	798,300	1.030	550	660	825
61/	121	8	893,100	1.090	600	720	900
61/	128	8	1,007,000	1.150	650	780	1000
91/	114	9	1,191,000	1.250	725	870	1135
91/	128	8	1,502,000	1.410	850	1020	1350
127/	114	9	1,660,000	1.480	900	1100	1460
127/	128	8	2,097,000	1.660	1100	1300	1700

*These individual strands are odd sizes not listed in the American Wire Tables.

CHAPTER 11

Detail Drawings

The difference between *assembly* drawings and *detail* drawings was pointed out in the preceding chapter.

Here the student should learn draughting procedure with respect to detail drawings—how many views are necessary,

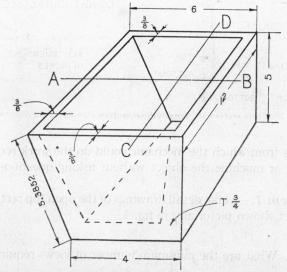

Fɪɢ. 1.—Pictorial of rectangular open top object.

what views, sections, sectional views, dimensioning, information, data, etc.

In the several examples given in this chapter the object will be shown in a pictorial drawing, such as cabinet or isometric projection, the problem being to make the necessary detail

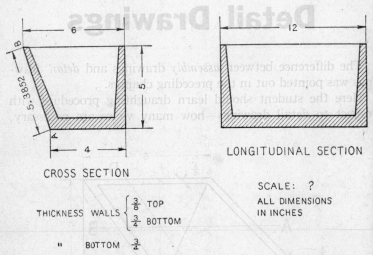

CROSS SECTION

LONGITUDINAL SECTION

SCALE: ?

ALL DIMENSIONS
IN INCHES

THICKNESS WALLS $\begin{cases} \frac{3}{8} \text{ TOP} \\ \frac{3}{4} \text{ BOTTOM} \end{cases}$

" BOTTOM $\frac{3}{4}$

Figs. 2 and 3.—*Cross section* and *longitudinal section* drawings of the object in fig. 1.

drawings from which the mechanic could do the work required to make or machine the object without asking questions.

Problem 1.—Make detail drawings of the open top rectangular object shown pictorially in fig. 1.

Ques. What are the minimum number of views required?

Ans. Two.

Ques. What two views would completely show the object?

Ans. A cross section and longitudinal section as in figs. 2 and 3.

Ques. Could any other view be added to make the print more easily readable?

Ans. The addition of a top plan would help to give a mental picture of the shape of the object but is not necessary.

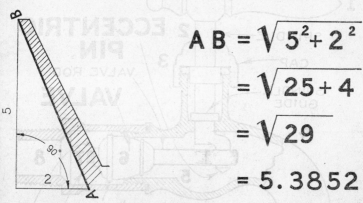

$$AB = \sqrt{5^2 + 2^2}$$
$$= \sqrt{25 + 4}$$
$$= \sqrt{29}$$
$$= 5.3852$$

Fig. 4.—Mathematical method of getting width of the inclined side of the object in fig. 1.

Ques. How is the width AB of the inclined side obtained?

Ans. Either by direct measurement on the drawing or by calculation as in fig. 4.

Ques. Which is the more accurate?

Ans. By calculation.

Ques. Why?

Ans. Because it is physically impossible to exactly measure anything.

Problem 2.—Make the necessary detail drawings for the Fuller faucet shown in fig. 5, and indicate the dimensioning without putting on actual dimensions. See figs. 6 to 16.

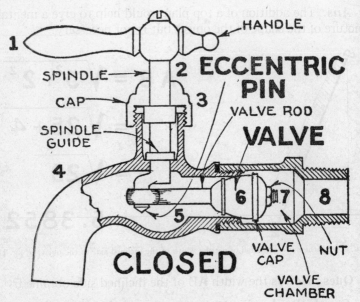

Fig. 5.—Fuller faucet.

Ques. How many detail drawings are required?

Ans. Fourteen, counting all views.

Ques. Why so many?

Ans. As indicated in the assembly drawing, fig. 5, there are

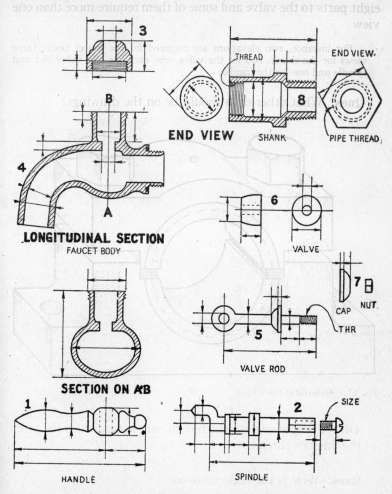

END VIEW

THREAD

3

B

A

LONGITUDINAL SECTION

FAUCET BODY

4

8

SHANK

PIPE THREAD

6

VALVE

7 B

CAP   NUT

THR

5

VALVE ROD

SECTION ON AB

1

HANDLE

2

SIZE

SPINDLE

FIGS. 6 to 16.—*Detailed drawings* of the Fuller faucet as shown in fig. 5.

eight parts to the valve and some of them require more than one view.

For instance, two elevations are required for the faucet body, three views for the shank, two for the valve, one each for the valve rod and spindle and one for the handle.

Ques. What other data should be on the drawings?

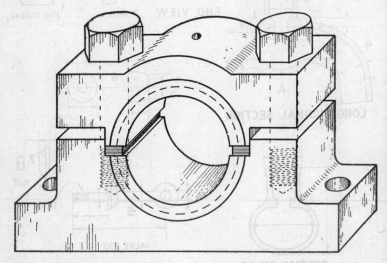

FIG. 17.—*Pictorial* of pillow block.

Ans. The material of which each part is made also the pitch of the various threads.

Ques. Why is the scale omitted?

Ans. Due to the reduction in size of the original drawings for this book the scales would have no meaning.

That is, a scale gives no indication of actual sizes on the drawing when reduced or enlarged from the size of the original drawing.

Problem 3.—Make detail drawings of the pillow block shown pictorially in fig. 17.

Ques. What is a pillow block?

Ans. A box or frame enclosing and supporting a brass journal or bearing in which a shaft revolves.

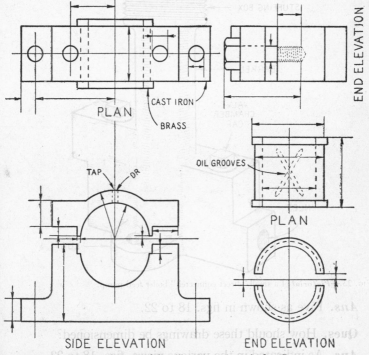

Figs. 18 to 22.—*Detail drawings* of the pillow block shown in fig. 17.

It generally consists of two parts, the box or block holding half of the brass and the cup holding the other half, the two halves being adjustable for wear.

Ques. How many detail drawings would ordinarily be made to completely show the pillow block of fig. 17?

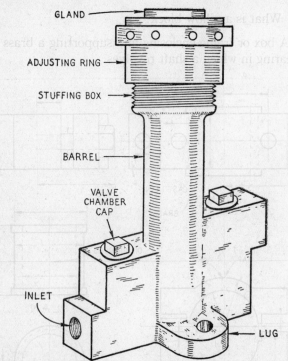

GLAND

ADJUSTING RING

STUFFING BOX

BARREL

VALVE
CHAMBER
CAP

INLET

LUG

Fig. 23.—*Pictorial* of a small "direct connected" boiler feed pump.

Ans. Five as shown in figs. 18 to 22.

Ques. How should these drawings be dimensioned?

Ans. As indicated in the various views, figs. 18 to 22.

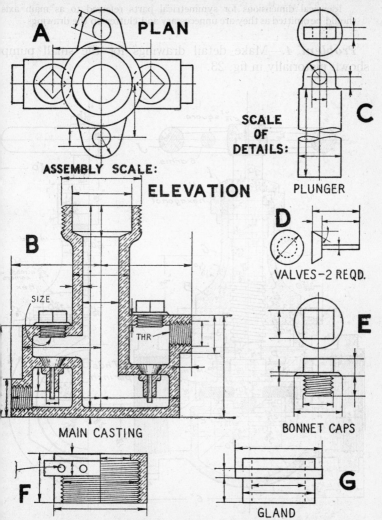

PLAN

A

ASSEMBLY SCALE:

ELEVATION

B

SIZE

THR

MAIN CASTING

SCALE OF DETAILS:

C

PLUNGER

D

VALVES—2 REQD.

E

BONNET CAPS

F

G

GLAND

Figs. 24 to 30.—*Detail drawings* of the feed pump shown in fig. 23.

Identical dimensions for symmetrical parts referred to as main axis should be omitted as they are unnecessary and clutter up the drawings.

Problem 4.—Make detail drawings for the small pump shown pictorially in fig. 23.

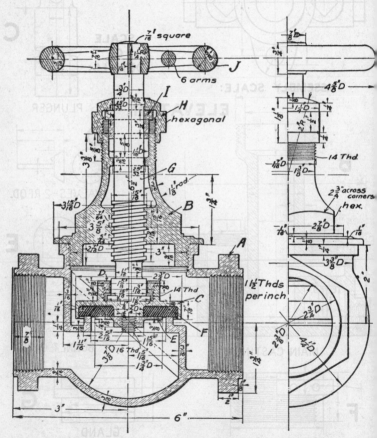

FIGS. 31 and 32.—*Side elevation* and *half end view* of a globe valve.

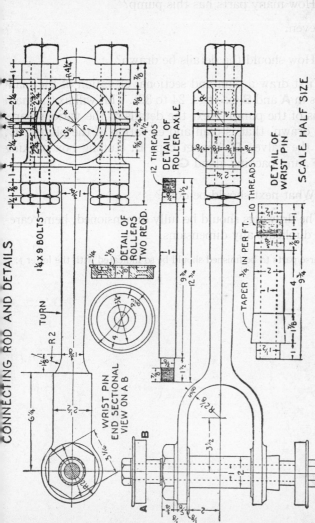

CONNECTING ROD AND DETAILS

WRIST PIN END SECTIONAL VIEW ON A B

DETAIL OF ROLLER AXLE

DETAIL OF ROLLERS TWO REQD.

DETAIL OF WRIST PIN

SCALE HALF SIZE

Figs. 33 to 38.—Connecting rod with detail of rollers, roller axle and wrist pin of Graham marine engine. The rollers transmit the lateral thrust to the guides, being used in place of gibs and is one of the unique features of the engine. Gibs are objectionable not only on account of friction but especially on account of their tendency to heat—in fact on some large engines the guides are water cooled. The object of the rollers is to avoid both of these objectionable features. *In operation* the rollers touch only one pair of guides at a time (depending on whether the engine be in forward or reverse motion) hence they run freely. This is obtained by adjusting the guides to say .002 in. clearance or about the thickness of a piece of tissue paper for the reverse guides, the forward guides being in contact with the rollers.

Ques. How many parts has this pump?

Ans. Seven.

Ques. How should the details be drawn?

Ans. First draw a plan and sectional elevation of the main asting, as in **A** and **B** (see figs. 24 to 30). This will fix the main dimensions of the pump. Next the details of the various parts should be drawn, that is plan and elevation of the plunger **C**, details of the valves **D**, bonnet caps **E**, stuffing box packing adjustor **F**, and packing gland **G**.

Ques. What next should be done?

Ans. The drawings should be fully dimensioned, being careful not to duplicate any dimensions.

Of course parts to be finished should be so indicated with the letter *f*.

CHAPTER 12

How to Sketch

Ques. What is a sketch?

Ans. A free hand drawing made with a pencil, from which mechanical drawings are subsequently elaborated.

Ques. To what does the term sketching especially apply?

Ans. To pictorial outlining.

Ques. What term for sketching would probably be more specific here?

Ans. Free hand drawing.

Ques. What is its applications?

Ans. It is for roughly making orthographic drawings, that is, without the aid of drawing instruments such as T square, triangles, etc., being guided by the eye alone.

The ability to quickly make a clear sketch is a valuable asset to the draughtsman and mechanic as well. Either may be called upon to sketch some details of a machine that is to be altered or upon which some improvement is to be made. Evidently such sketch or sketches are of no use to the designer unless they contain all the dimensions and data necessary for re-designing the part.

Ques. What hardness of lead should be used?

Ans. It depends upon the character of the drawing and the precision required.

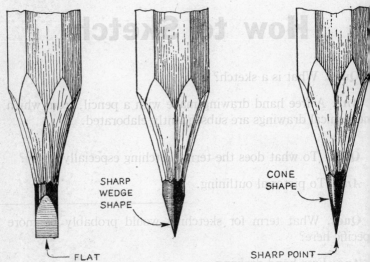

SHARP WEDGE SHAPE

CONE SHAPE

FLAT

SHARP POINT

Figs. 1 and 2.—*Side* and *end views* of pencil with lead sharpened to a chisel or wedge shape.

Fig. 3.—View of pencil with lead sharpened to a long conical point.

Some draughtsmen recommend a 2H pencil, but this is pretty soft for accurate work. A 4H is better, even a 6H is used sometimes.

Ques. What is the objection to hard pencils?

Ans. The harder the pencil the more difficult it is to see the lines.

How to Sharpen Pencils.—There are two methods of sharpening a drawing pencil, classed with respect to the shape given the lead, as

1. Flat or chisel
2. Conical

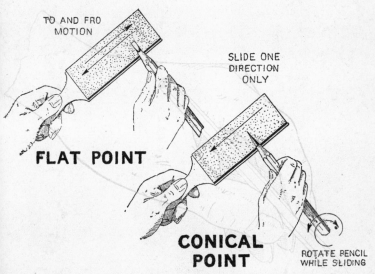

Fig. 4.—Method of sharpening pencil for flat or chisel point.

Fig. 5.—Method of sharpening pencil for conical point.

Ques. What is done preliminary to sharpening the lead?

Ans. The wood is cut down cone shaped, being careful not to cut the lead.

Ques. Describe the two shapes of lead generally used.

Ans. Figs. 1 to 3 show these shapes.

Ques. How is a pencil sharpened to the flat or chisel shape?

Ans. Slide the lead (at a very acute angle) along the pad, forming it to the chisel shape as in fig. 4.

Ques. How is a pencil sharpened to a conical or round point?

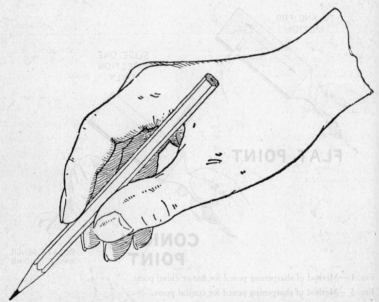

FIG. 6.—*Approved position* of holding pencil for free hand drawing. Do not grasp pencil too near lead point, the object being to multiply the movement given the pencil by the fingers. In practice, note difficulty in drawing straight lines introduced when pencil is held very near the point.

Ans. Slide the lead over the pad in one direction, turning it on its axis during the movement along the pad, as in fig. 5.

Ques. What might be said with respect to a dull pencil?

Ans. Do not expect to do good work with a pencil having an 'acre of lead" at its point.

Ques. What movement should be given to a pencil with conical point in drawing lines?

Ans. After drawing a line, slightly rotate the pencil before drawing another line.

This helps to keep the pencil sharp.

Method of Holding Pencil.—Much depends upon correctly holding the pencil. The proper way is shown in fig. 6.

The pencil should be held firmly between the thumb and first finger of the right hand; press the second finger against the pencil at the opposite side to the thumb pressure, so that the pencil is firmly held by the contact of the thumb and two fingers—the third and fourth fingers just coming into easy reach of the paper surface— the wrist or ball of the hand resting lightly on the surface of the work, the arm resting on the desk or drawing board for steadiness.

Ques. How is the motion of the pencil produced for vertical stroke?

Ans. It is produced from the movement of the fingers and thumb.

Ques. For horizontal strokes?

Ans. By fingers and thumb combined with a wrist or elbow motion.

Ques. How are oblique lines produced?

Ans. By a free movement with nothing cramped or confined about the finger joints.

Ques. What precaution should be taken in holding the pencil?

Ans. Do not hold the pencil too close to the end.

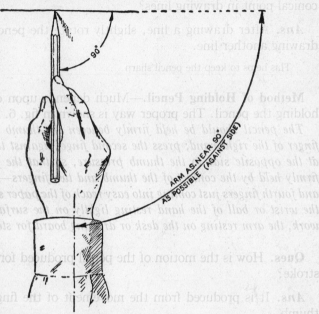

Fig. 7.—*Horizontal line position.* Note pencil at 90° to line to be drawn, arm as near the same angle as possible, that is, against the side.

Ques. Why?

Ans. By letting it project sufficiently beyond the fingers, the movement given by the fingers is multiplied and this helps in drawing straight lines.

How to Draw Free Hand.—It is essential in order to attain proficiency in making clear and legible sketches that the draughtsman can draw straight lines and "round circles." He must be able to draw lines in various positions as:

1. Horizontal
2. Vertical

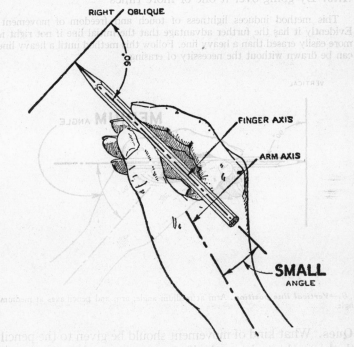

FIG. 8.—*Right oblique line position.* Arm at small angle. Finger and arm axes at small angle.

3. Oblique to right
4. Oblique to left

Horizontal Lines.—Hold the pencil as in fig. 7 keeping the elbow near the side. Produce the line by one *light* steady stroke, the movement being obtained by motion of the wrist.

Ques. How is the required width of the line obtained?

Ans. By going over it one or more times

This method induces lightness of touch and freedom of movement. Evidently it has the further advantage that the initial line if not right is more easily erased than a heavy line. Follow this method until a heavy line can be drawn without the necessity of erasing.

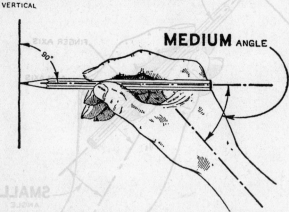

VERTICAL

MEDIUM ANGLE

90°

FIG. 9.—*Vertical line position.* Arm at medium angle; arm and pencil axes at medium angle.

Ques. What kind of movement should be given to the pencil with the single stroke method?

Ans. The movement should be even throughout, that is, not made with a jerky movement.

Ques. Describe the progressive method of drawing lines.

Ans. In this method the line is drawn by several short strokes, each stroke producing part of the line.

The student should practice both methods just described, adopting the one that presents the least difficulty.

Right Oblique Lines.—Hold the pencil as in fig. 8, with elbow a little from the side. Draw the line with one light stroke by a movement of the fingers and thumb, repeating the strokes until the line is as heavy as desired.

Ques. What should be avoided in drawing oblique lines and why?

Ans. Do not draw an oblique line by using the wrist or elbow as a "hinge" with fingers rigid as the tendency of such movements is to produce arcs.

Ques. What does wrist movement produce?

Ans. An arc of short radius.

Ques. How is an arc of long radius produced?

Ans. By using the elbow as a hinge for the movement.

Ques. How may the proper movement be detected?

Ans. By watching the action of the thumb. If it bend as the line is being drawn, the correct movement is obtained.

Left Oblique Lines.—Hold the pencil as in fig. 19 with elbow removed far from the side. The correct distance is when the arm is at an angle of 90° to the line to be drawn.

Ques. How are left oblique lines drawn?

Ans. With a movement of the fingers and thumb.

Vertical Lines.—To draw a vertical line requires more care than the lines just described. Hold the pencil as in fig. 9 with elbow moved well out from the side and draw line by a movement of the fingers and thumb.

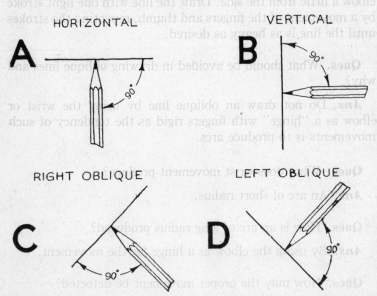

Figs. 10 to 13.—*Position of pencil* always at 90° to line to be drawn, showing; A, horizontal; B, vertical; C, right oblique, and D, left oblique line.

Ques. What is the usual tendency in drawing vertical lines?

Ans. The tendency to draw vertical lines slightly inclined to the horizontal instead of perpendicular.

Ques. How is this tendency overcome?

Ans. Place the paper in such position that the line when drawn will be exactly in front of the eyes.

Summary.—It will be noticed that each change in direction of the line to be drawn, has been accompanied with a corresponding change in the position of the elbow and wrist.

Note the following with respect to position of elbow:

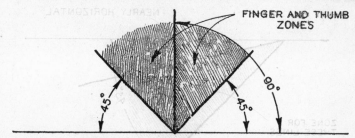

FIG. 14.—*Finger* and *thumb* lines.

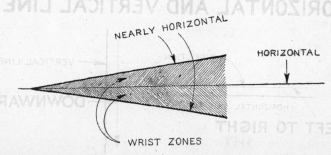

FIG. 15.—*Wrist* lines.

1. Horizontal line, elbow near side

2. Right oblique line, elbow a little removed

3. Vertical line, elbow more removed

4. Left oblique line, elbow most removed

EITHER FINGER AND THUMB OR WRIST LINES

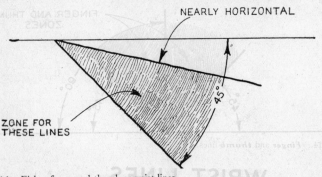

FIG. 16.—Either finger and thumb or wrist lines.

HORIZONTAL AND VERTICAL LINES

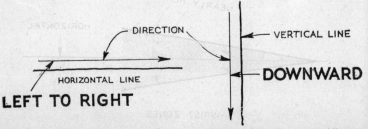

FIG. 17.—*Direction of pencil movement. 1.* in drawing horizontal and vertical lines.

In general, when a straight line is to be sketched, it should be at right angles to some such line as is shown in figs. 10 to 13.

Line Producing Movements Classified. — With respect to the movements by which lines are drawn, they may be classed as:

1. Finger movements . . . Fig.

2. *Wrist* . . .

In addition, lines may be drawn by either finger and thumb or wrist movement.

Ques. How are lines 0° to 30° from the horizontal drawn?

Ans. By finger and thumb movement, as in fig. 14.

Ques. How are lines horizontal or nearly horizontal drawn?

Ans. By wrist movement, as in fig. 15.

Rules for Direction of the Movement. — As regards the direction in which the pencil is moved, depending on the inclination of the line, the rules are as follows:

1. Horizontal lines, left to right . . .

2. Vertical lines . . .

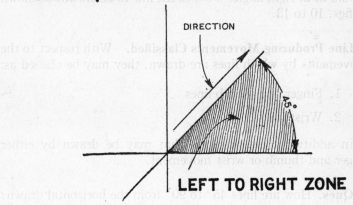

FIG. 18.—*Direction of pencil movement, 2,* in drawing right oblique lines 0° to 45°.

Arcs and Circles. — The correct position of the hand in describing an arc is that which would be required for drawing a straight line joining its extremities as shown in fig. 20. Note that the pencil is held inside or outside of the arc according to

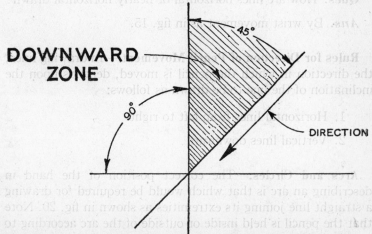

FIG. 19.—*Direction of pencil movement, 3,* in drawing left oblique lines 45° to 90°.

In general, with respect to the position of the pencil, it should be at right angles (90°) to the line to be drawn, as shown in figs. 10 to 13.

Line Producing Movements Classified.—With respect to the movements by which lines are drawn, they may be classed as:

1. Finger and thumb lines
2. Wrist lines

In addition there are lines that may be drawn by either finger and thumb or wrist movement.

Ques. How are lines 45° to 90° from the horizontal drawn?

Ans. By finger and thumb movement, as in fig. 14.

Ques. How are lines horizontal or nearly horizontal drawn?

Ans. By wrist movement as in fig. 15.

Rules for Direction of Pencil Movement.—In drawing lines, the direction in which the pencil is moved, depends upon the inclination of the line to be drawn as follows:

1. Horizontal lines from left to right
2. Vertical lines downward

Arcs and Circles.—The correct position of the hand in describing an arc is that which would be required for drawing a straight line joining its extremities as shown in fig. 20. Note that the pencil is held inside or outside of the arc according to position of the arc.

There are several methods of describing a circle as by:

1. Guide marks on axes

2. Inscribing in square

3. Preliminary pencil movement

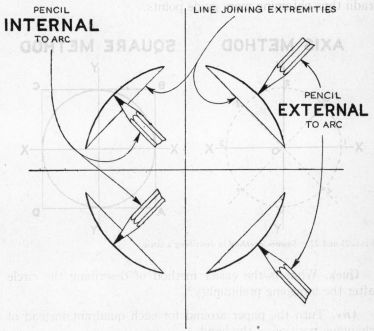

PENCIL
INTERNAL
TO ARC

LINE JOINING EXTREMITIES

PENCIL
EXTERNAL
TO ARC

FIG. 20.—*Pencil position* in describing arcs in the four quadrants,

Ques. Describe the first method.

Ans. In fig. 21 draw the rectangular axes XX and YY, and space off on them by eye the equal distances 01, 02, etc., equal radius of circle to be described. Then describe circle through these points.

Ques. What should be done for greater accuracy?

Ans. Draw the diagonal axis indicated by dotted lines, spacing off on them *oa*, *ob*, etc., of same length as the other radii thus obtaining more guide points.

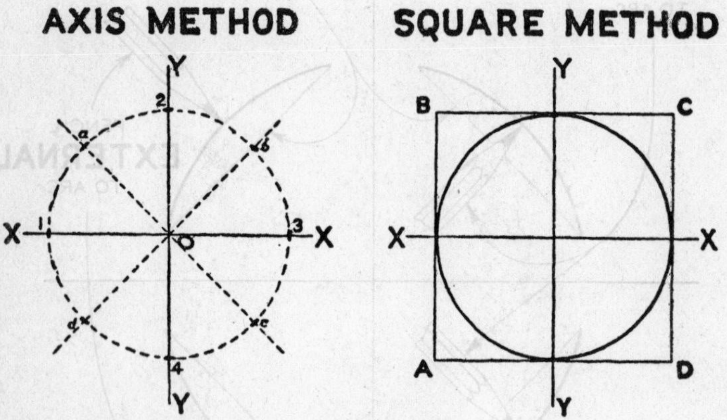

AXIS METHOD   SQUARE METHOD

Figs. 21 and 22.—*Square method* in describing a circle.

Ques. What is the easier method of describing the circle after the foregoing preliminary?

Ans. Turn the paper around for each quadrant instead of changing position of the hand.

It is not always convenient to shift the paper, hence the student should acquire sufficient technique on circles so as not to resort to shifting the paper.

Ques. Describe the square method of describing circles.

Ans. In fig. 22 draw a square ABCD symmetrical with rectangular axes XX and YY.

This then is made up of four little squares each of which will serve as a guide in describing the circle progressively with 90° arcs, the completed circle being tangent to the four sides of the large square.

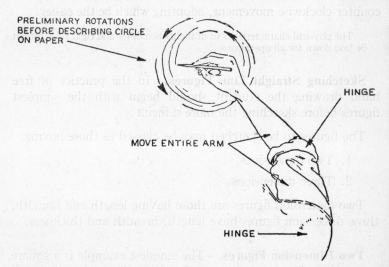

PRELIMINARY ROTATIONS BEFORE DESCRIBING CIRCLE ON PAPER

HINGE

MOVE ENTIRE ARM

HINGE

FIG. 23.—*Preliminary pencil movement* in describing a circle.

Ques. Describe the preliminary pencil movement method of describing circles.

Ans. As in fig. 23 it consists of rotating the pencil several times before contact with the paper, the radius of rotation of course being that of the desired circle.

In the case of a small circle, this can be done by finger movement, but for a large circle the hand should be rigid and the movement obtained from the entire arm with the elbow as a hinge.

In the preliminary rotation, make as many turns as necessary until the pencil point describes the nearest approach to a circle of the desired diameter, then let the pencil point contact with the paper.

Ques. Describe methods of preliminary movement practice.

Ans. Practice with clockwise movement and then with counter-clockwise movement, adopting which be the easier.

The physical characteristics of draughtsmen differ and rigid rules cannot be laid down for all operations.

Sketching Straight Line Figures.—In the practice of free hand drawing the student should begin with the simplest figures before sketching the more difficult.

The figures to be sketched may be classed as those having:

1. Two dimensions
2. Three dimensions

Two dimension figures are those having length and breadth; three dimension figures have length, breadth and thickness.

Two Dimension Figures.—The simplest example is a square or rectangle. To sketch a square first locate two points as A and B, in fig. 24, at a horizontal distance apart, equal to a side of the square. Place points C and D exactly under B and A, at a distance equal to AB. That is, make AD and BC equal to AB.

Now in fig. 25 join AB and DC, then join AD and BC.

Evidently by joining the lines in the order of parallel pairs less effort is required than if joined in such order as AB, AD, DC, and BC. Note in this order the position of the arm must be changed laterally four times.

It is not the intention of the author to fill this chapter with a multiplicity of geometrical problems, but to give only a few typical figures to serve as practice examples in sketching. In fact the student is here learning to draw free hand and not geometry.

Exercise.—Find the center of a square.

Having drawn a square as directed in figs. 24 and 25, draw the two diagonals AC and BD. The point O, where they intersect is the center of the square, as in fig. 26.

Ellipses.—A curved figure which the draughtsman must sketch frequently is the *ellipse*.

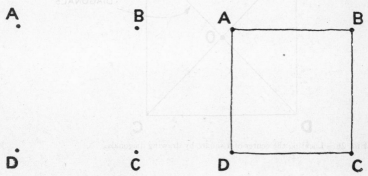

FIGS. 24 and 25.—Method of drawing a square free hand.

Ques. What is an ellipse?

Ans. A projection of a circle on a plane oblique to that of the circle, as shown pictorially in fig. 27.

Ques. What is the mathematical definition of an ellipse?

Ans. A plane curve such that the sum of the distances from any point on the curve to two fixed points is a constant.

Ques. What are the two fixed points called?

Ans. The *foci*.

Ques. Name the two diameters of an ellipse.

Ans. The longest diameter of the ellipse is called the *major axis* and the shortest diameter the *minor axis*.

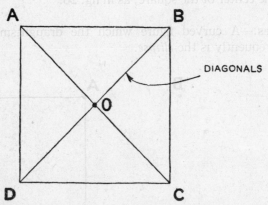

FIG. 26.—Locating the center of a square by drawing diagonals.

Ques. What is the relation between the major and minor axes of an ellipse?

Ans. They bisect each other at right angles in a point called the center.

Ques. What are the two limits as to form of an ellipse?

Ans. Its contour may vary from a straight line to a circle.

Ques. Define diameter of an ellipse.

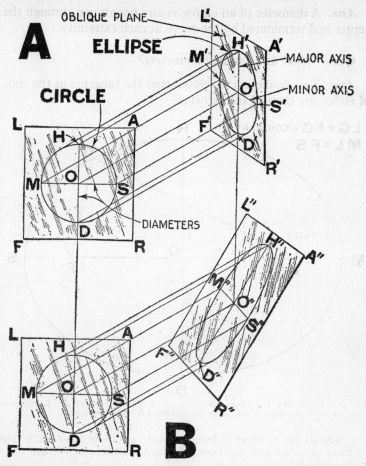

FIG. 27.—*Pictorial definition of an ellipse.* At **A**, is parallel to a diameter of the circle. At **B**, no axis of ellipse parallel to diameter of the circle. Points on the ellipse are obtained by projecting points from the circle over to the oblique plane. Thus at **A**, points as **M**, **H**, **S** and **D** are projected over to the oblique plane by lines **MM'**, **HH'**, **SS'**, and **DD'**, parallel to the center line **OO'**, cutting the oblique plane in points **M'**, **H'**, **S'** and **D'**. A curve drawn through these points will be *an ellipse or the projection of the circle on the oblique plane.*

Ans. A diameter of an ellipse is any line drawn through the center and terminated by the curve at each extremity.

Ques. What are conjugal diameters?

Ans. Two diameters so related that the tangents at the ends of either are parallel to the other.

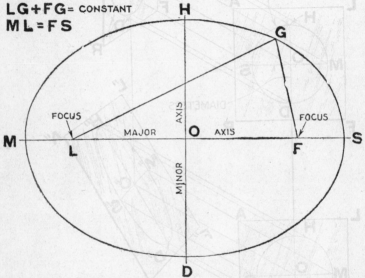

LG+FG= CONSTANT
ML=FS

FIG. 28.—Ellipse, **MS**, major axis; **HD**, minor axis. **L** and **F**, are the foci and **G**, any point on the curve. An ellipse is defined by the equation **LG+GF**=constant.

Ellipses can be drawn in infinite variety, as to length and width. The major and minor axes may have any imaginable difference in length.

By holding a penny first in nearly a vertical position and then gradually turning it round until hardly any of the surface is visible, the circular edge of the coin presents every conceivable change in the form of an ellipse.

Ques. Name some methods of describing ellipses.

Ans. 1. Free hand; 2, semi-free hand; 3, plotting points.

Free Hand Ellipses.—Attempts to describe an ellipse by the preliminary movement method usually results in figures more distorted than elliptical, and it is a good draughtsman who can describe an ellipse with any degree of accuracy by this method.

Ques. How is an ellipse described by the free hand method?

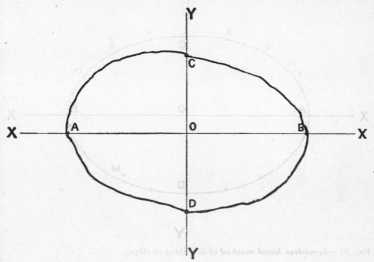

FIG. 29.—*Free hand method* of describing an ellipse.

Ans. Draw, as in fig. 29, rectangular axes XX and YY intersection at O. By eye mark off the major and minor axes AB and CD, making OA=OB and OC=OD. Then by the preliminary movement method (already described) using elliptical instead of circular motion, try to approximate the ellipse, as shown in fig. 29.

The difficulty is apparent by the distorted figure. This method is better adapted to small ellipses without trying to describe about their axes.

Semi-Free Hand Ellipses.—This is strictly speaking a free hand method, but a series of guide points are first located by eye and the curve described by progressive short strokes.

Ques. Describe the free hand method.

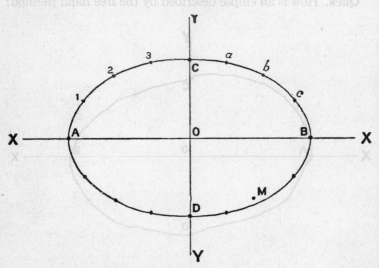

Fig. 30.—*Semi-free hand method* of describing an ellipse.

Ans. First draw the axes as in fig. 30; then locate by eye a series of guiding points as 1, 2, 3, *a*, *b*, *c*, etc., as judged "by eye" to be on the curve. The best way to get these points near the correct position is to try to see the entire curve mentally.

The final step is to describe with short strokes a curve through these points. Any point that is evidently "off" as at M, fair up the curve by drawing around it either outside or inside.

Ellipse with Plotted Points.—This is a semi-mechanical method in which points lying on the curve are obtained mechanically and the curve described through these points free hand. A very close approximation can be obtained by this method.

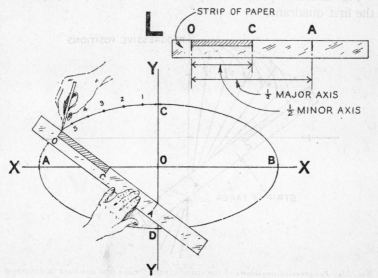

FIGS. 31 and 32.—*Semi-mechanical method* of describing an ellipse by plotting points on the curve.

Ques. Describe the method with plotted points.

Ans. First draw the rectangular axes XX and YY as in fig. 31. Lay off OA and OC half major and minor axes respectively. It is not necessary to lay off the other halves of these axes as they will be automatically located in plotting more accurately than by eye.

On a strip of paper mark OA = ½ major axis and OC = ½ minor axis as at L. Place the strip of paper in progressive positions so that the point C, is always on the major axis and the point A, on the minor axis, making a dot for each position as 1, 2, 3, etc. Through the points thus obtained sketch in the curve by short progressive strokes. Repeat for each quadrant thus completing the ellipse.

Fig. 33 shows progressive positions of the strip of paper for the first quadrant.

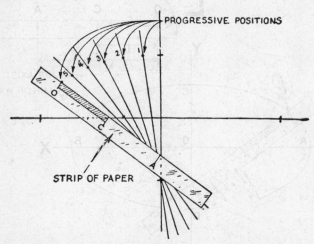

FIG. 33.—*Progressive positions* of the strip of paper for the first quadrant in describing an ellipse by plotting.

Three Dimension Figures.—The term three dimension relates to figures having: 1, length; 2, breadth, and 3, thickness.

Ques. What is the simplest example of a three dimension figure?

Ans. A cube.

In a cube any of the three dimensions may be called length, breadth or thickness. but in elongated figures these terms are more specific.

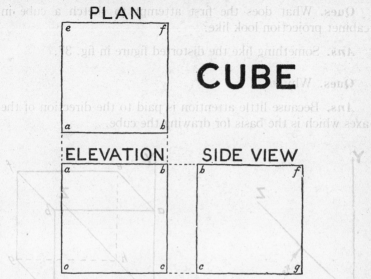

Fig. 34 to 36.—*Orthographic views* of a cube.

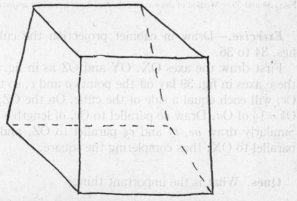

Fig. 37.—Usual result in first attempts to sketch in cabinet projection.

Ques. What does the first attempt to sketch a cube in cabinet projection look like?

Ans. Something like the distorted figure in fig. 37.

Ques. Why?

Ans. Because little attention is paid to the direction of the axes which is the basis for drawing the cube.

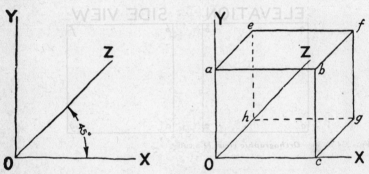

FIGS. 38 and 39.—Method of drawing a cube free hand in *cabinet projection*.

Exercise.—Draw in cabinet projection the cube shown in figs. 34 to 36.

First draw the axes OX, OY and OZ as in fig. 38. Now on these axes in fig. 39 lay off the points *a* and *c*, so that O*a*, and O*c*, will each equal a side of the cube. On the OZ, axis lay off O*h* = ½ of O*a*. Draw *ab* parallel to O*c*, of length = O*c*. Join *bc*. Similarly draw *ae*, *bf* and *cg* parallel to OZ, and *ef*, and *hg*, parallel to OX, thus completing the square.

Ques. What is the important thing?

Ans. Parallelism.

That is axis OX lines must be parallel to OX, axis OY lines parallel to OY, etc.

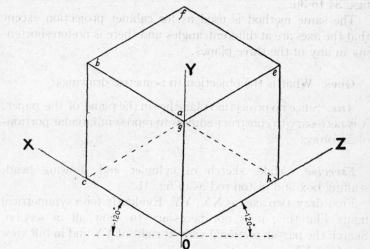

Fig. 40.—Sketch of cube in *isometric projection*.

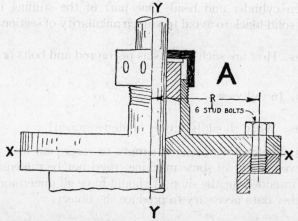

Fig. 41.—Typical example of sketching machine details.

Exercise.—Draw in isometric projection the cube shown in figs. 34 to 36.

The same method is used as for cabinet projection except that the axes are at different angles and there is no foreshortening in any of the three planes.

Ques. What is the objection to isometric drawings?

Ans. Since no projection plane lies in the plane of the paper, it is necessary to construct ellipses to represent circular portions of an object.

Exercise.—Make sketch of cylinder end showing head, stuffing box and piston rod as in fig. 41.

First draw two axes as XX, YY. Evidently for a symmetrical figure like this, it is not necessary to show all in section. Sketch the part in sectional view at right of YY and in full view at left of YY.

The horizontal axis here serves well for the dividing line between cylinder and head. One part of the stuffing box is shown solid black to avoid too much angularity of section lines.

Ques. How are such objects as piston rod and bolts or studs shown?

Ans. In full view.

Ques. When should sketches be dimensioned?

Ans. Sketches if intended simply to record an idea, as in the development of some machine, need not be dimensioned, but if intended for the shop, it should have all dimensions and any other data necessary to produce the object.

CHAPTER 13

Surfaces

In such work as pattern cutting or sheet metal work, surfaces are divided into two general classes known as:

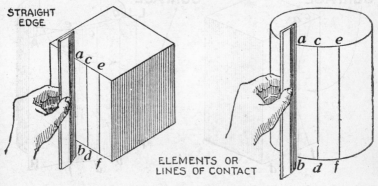

FIGS. 1 and 2.—Plane and curved elementary surfaces.

1. Elementary
2. Warped

Ques. What is an elementary surface?

Ans. A surface in which a straight edge may be placed in continuous contact with the surface as for instance in positions *ab*, *cd*, *ef*, of either fig. 1 or fig. 2.

Ques. What is the line of contact of the straight edge called?

Ans. An element of the surface.

Ques. What are consecutive elements of the surface?

Ans. Elements which lie infinitely close to each other.

Ques. What are the characteristics of elementary **and** warped developments?

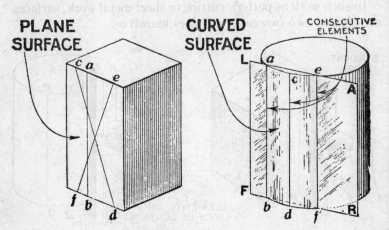

Figs. 3 and 4.—Distinction between plane and curved surfaces.

Ans. An object with an elementary surface may be developed accurately, but one with a warped surface, only approximately.

That is to say, objects having elementary surfaces may be formed by simply folding or rolling the metal pattern, whereas if the object have a warped surface, the metal pattern must undergo the operation of *raising* or *bumping* to bring the pattern to the true shape of the object when folded or rolled.

Ques. Name two kinds of elementary surfaces.

Ans. Plane and curved as shown in figs. 3 and 4.

Ques. What is a plane surface?

Ans. One in which elements may be drawn in any direction as in fig. 3.

Ques. What is a curved surface?

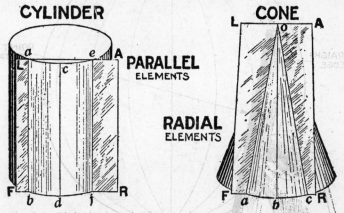

FIGS. 5 and 6.—Distinction between *cylindrical* and *conical* surfaces. Fig. 5, elements parallel; fig. 6, elements radial. Both surfaces being curved surfaces, no three consecutive elements lie in the same plane as indicated by plane LARF, passing through the first and third of the three consecutive elements *ab*, *cd*, and *ef*.

Ans. One in which no three consecutive elements lie in the same plane as in fig. 4.

In the figure let *ab*, *cd* and *ef* be three consecutive elements, then if a plane LARF pass through *ab* and *ef*, the intervening element *cd* will not lie in this plane. The curved surface shown in fig. 4 is a *cylindrical* surface or curved surface having parallel elements, as distinguished from another class of curved surfaces which does not have parallel elements, as for instance a conical surface

Ques. What is a cylindrical surface?

Ans. A surface having parallel elements. No three consecutive elements lie in the same plane. Fig. 5 is a cylindrical surface.

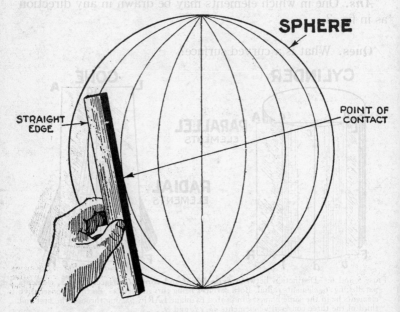

Fig. 7.—*Warped surface* or surface in which a straight edge can be placed in contact only at a point.

Ques. What is a conical surface?

Ans. A surface having radial elements meeting in a common point, no three consecutive elements lie in the same plane. Fig. 6 is a conical surface.

Ques. What is a warped surface?

Ans. A surface in which a straight edge may be placed in contact only at a point.

For instance the sphere shown in fig. 7.

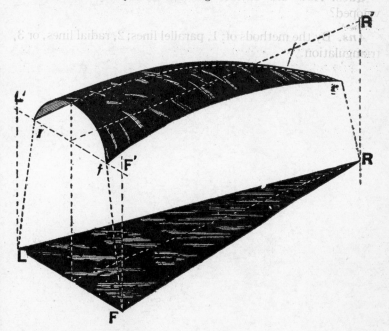

FIG. 8.—*Approximate pattern* as cut for a section of a warped surface showing shape of pattern before and after warping.

Ques. What is the characteristic of patterns for warped surfaces?

Ans. They can be cut only to the approximate shape as for instance in fig. 8.

Here, the pattern **LFR** for a section of a warped surface, must be warped or hammered to the shape *lfr* so that its surface will coincide with the warped surface. The figure clearly shows the shape of the pattern before and after warping. Note *lf*, brought in from **L′F′** and *r*, lowered from **R′**

Ques. How are objects having elementary surfaces developed?

Ans. By the methods of: 1, parallel lines; 2, radial lines, or 3, triangulation.

FIG. —Approximate pattern as cut for a section of a warped surface, showing form of pattern before and after warping.

Ques. What is the characteristic of patterns for warped surfaces?

Ans. They can be cut only to the approximate shape as for instance in fig. 8.

CHAPTER 14

Development by Parallel Lines

In any development, a plan and elevation of the object is first drawn, and from these views the development, that is, the developed shape of the object, is obtained by laying off what is called a *stretch out*.

Ques. What is a stretch out?

Ans. Simply the outline of the object unfolded and laid out flat.

Development of a Prismoid.—The prismoid as shown in fig. 1 is here selected for the first example. Note carefully the general shape of the solid, especially the shape of the sides.

To develop, draw in fig. 3 a base line at the elevation of the base and on this base line lay off points 1, 2, 3, 4 and 1. The distances between these points are obtained from the plan. The distance between points 1 and 2, in stretch out equal distance between points 1 and 2, in plan; between 2 and 3, in stretch out equal distance between 2 and 3, in plan, and so on all the way around to the starting point 1. Erect perpendiculars at the points thus obtained and project over points A, B, C, D, and A, from the elevation by the dotted lines parallel to the base line. The intersections of these dotted lines with the perpendiculars give the heights of the perpendiculars corresponding to the heights of the edges of the prismoid, that is, A1, in stretch out equal A1, in elevation; B2, in stretch out equal B2, in elevation, etc.

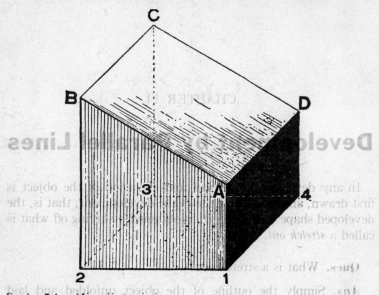

Fig. 1.—*Prismoid* in *cabinet projection*.

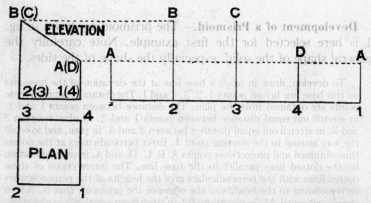

Figs. 2 to 4.—*Development of pattern* by *parallel lines* for the prismoid shown in fig. 1; base line and perpendiculars.

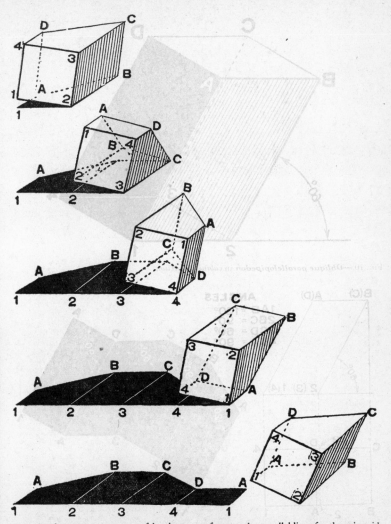

Figs. 5 to 9.—*Moving picture* of development of pattern by parallel lines for the prismoid of fig. 1; showing prismoid rolling over on its sides and pattern progressively developed

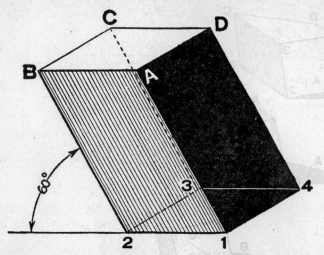

FIG. 10.—*Oblique parallelopipedon* in *cabinet projection.*

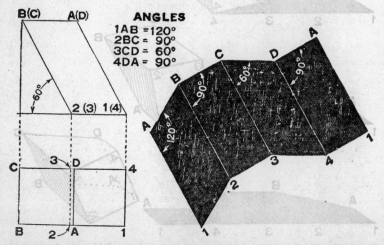

ANGLES
1AB = 120°
2BC = 90°
3CD = 60°
4DA = 90°

FIGS. 11 to 13.—*Development of pattern* by *parallel lines* for the oblique parallelopipedon shown in fig. 10. Case 1. Development on line A1.

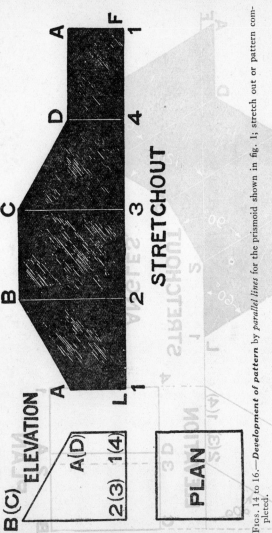

FIGS. 14 to 16.—*Development of pattern* by *parallel lines* for the prismoid shown in fig. 1; stretch out or pattern completed.

The stretch out is now completed by joining the points A, B, C, D and A. The completed stretch out is shown in fig. 15. The moving picture (figs. 5 to 9) shows the progressive development of the pattern.

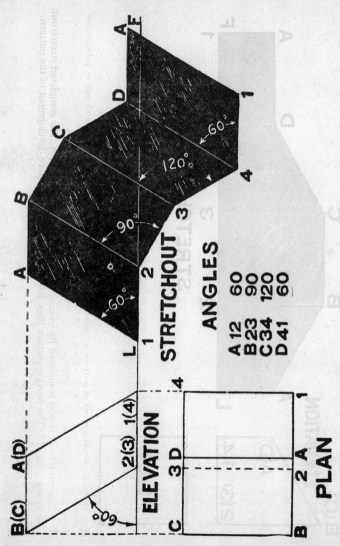

FIGS. 17 to 19.—*Development of pattern* by *parallel lines* for the oblique parallelopipedon shown in fig. 13. Case 2. Development referred to base line.

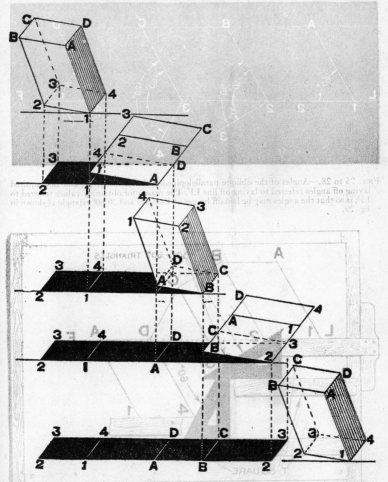

Figs. 20 to 24.—**Moving picture** of development of pattern by *parallel lines* for the oblique parallelopipedon of fig. 10, showing the parallelopipedon rolling over on its sides and pattern progressively developed.

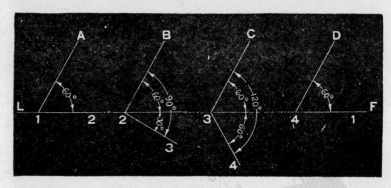

Figs. 25 to 28.—Angles of the oblique parallelopipedon shown in fig. 10, and the required laying off angles referred to laying off line LF. The reason for obtaining values referred to LF, is so that the angles may be laid off by use of T square and 30-60° triangle as shown in fig. 29.

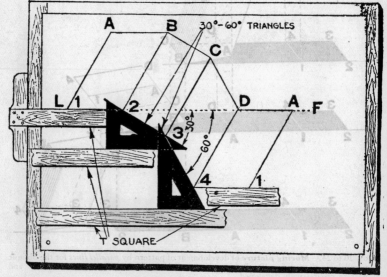

Fig. 29.—*Method of laying out angles* in the developments by the use of T square and 30°, 60° triangle.

Example.—Develop a pattern for the sides of the oblique parallelopipedon shown in fig. 10.

Case 1. Development on line A1; *Case 2,* Development referred to base line.

Case 1.—First draw an elevation and plan of the parallelopipedon in orthographic projection as shown in figs. 11 and 13, lettering these views to correspond with the numbers and letters of fig. 10.

Draw A1, equal to and parallel to A1, in elevation. Draw 12, equal to 12, in elevation making angle A12, equal 60° continue as indicated

Case 2.—Draw in elevation and plan as in Case 1, and continue base 21 of elevation, giving a base line of reference LF, to which the angles are referred, as shown in figs. 17 to 19.

On LF, lay off points 1 and 2, spaced as in the elevation. Through 1 draw a line at an angle of 60° with LF, and project over point A in elevation, giving length 1A, on stretch out equal to length 1A in elevation. Through points 2 and A draw lines parallel to 1A and 12, respectively, completing the first section of the pattern 1AB2, in stretch out which is the development of one side of solid.

Construct in a similar manner the remaining sections thus completing the stretch out 1ABCDA14321.

FIG. 30.—*Cabinet projection* of cylinder of revolution cut by plane inclined 45° to the base.

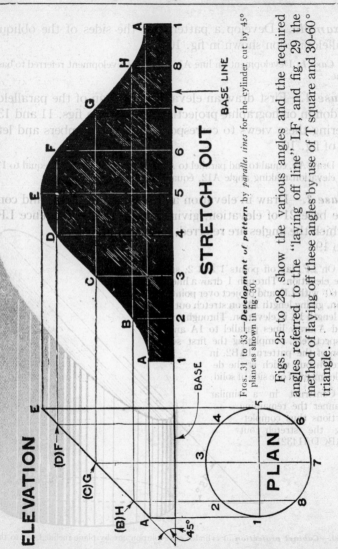

ELEVATION

PLAN

BASE

STRETCH OUT

BASE LINE

45°

FIGS. 31 to 33.—*Development of pattern by parallel lines* for the cylinder cut by 45° plane as shown in fig. 30.

Figs. 25 to 28 show the various angles and the required angles referred to the "laying off line", LF, and fig. 29 the method of laying off these angles by use of T square and 30-60° triangle.

Example.—Develop a pattern for cylindrical surface of the cut cylinder shown in fig. 30.

In fig. 31, take any number of points on the circle as 1, 2, 3, 4, 5, 6, 7 and 8, and project up in elevation obtaining points A(I), B(H), C(G), D(F) and E. Here some of the points coincide, that is some lie directly back of the others. Thus point 2, or its projection (B), lies back of 8, or its projection H, the parentheses indicating the fact.

Draw base line for the stretch out and lay off on this line points 1, 2, 3, 4, 5, 6, 7, 8, 1, spaced equal to the lengths of the arcs between points 1, 2; 2, 3; etc., in plan.

In the stretch out erect perpendiculars through the points 1, 2, 3, etc., and project over from elevation, points A, B (H), C (G), D (F), and E, giving points A, B, C, D, E, F, G, H, A. Draw a curve through these points which completes the stretch out. Note carefully in projecting over points from elevation, their location on stretch out. Thus point (B), is projected to perpendicular through 2, and point H, to perpendicular through 8; this is evident from the plan.

Where a large number of points are taken, the length of the spacing of the point in stretch out may be obtained by setting the dividers by the chord method as in fig. 34, but it should be understood that this is only an approximation and the stretch out will never be the full length no matter how many points are taken.

For precision, especially where only a few points are taken (as in fig. 31) the dividers should be set by calculation, called line setting (figs. 35 and 36). A comparison of the two methods is shown in figs. 37 and 38. To illustrate the method of line setting suppose the diameter of the cylinder be 6 ins. and the 8 points be taken as in fig. 35. Then

$$\text{circumference} = 6 \times 3.1416 = 18.85 \text{ ins.}$$

that is, the length of the stretch out = 18.85 and the distance between points = 18.85 ÷ 8 = 2.36 ins. Draw a line and measure off accurately a distance LF = 18.85 ins.

Now set dividers to 2.36 ins. and make a trial spacing. The result obtained will probably be as on line A. Note magnitude of the error. Make additional trials as indicated on lines B, C, D, etc., until the true setting is obtained as on line LF.

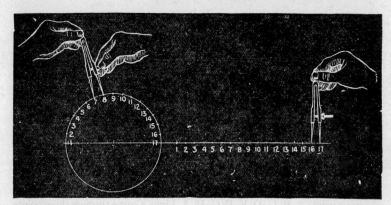

Fig. 34 —*Chord method* of spacing.

their completed. The stretch-out. Note .... on elevation, their location on stretch out. This point (B), is projected perpendicular through 2, and point B to perpendicular through 8; this is evident from the plan.

Where a large number .... the length of the spacing of the dividers by the chord method as in fig. 34, but it should be understood that this is only an approximation and the stretch-out will not be the full length no matter how many points are taken.

For precision, especially where only a few points are taken .... the dividers should be set by .... stepped line .... 36). A comparison of the two .... shown in figs. 37, 38. To set .... and the 8 points be taken as in fig. 35. Then

$$\text{circumference} = 6 \times \pi = 18.85 \text{ ins.}$$

Thus, the depth of the stretch-out = 18.85 and the distance between points = $18.85 \div 8 = 2.36$ ins. Dividers cannot measure off accurately a length = 2.36 ins.

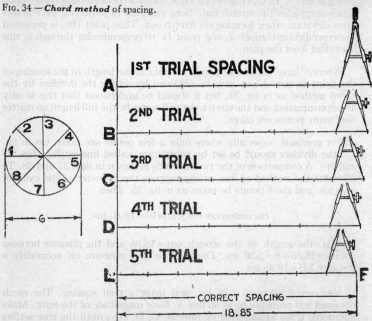

The result obtained will probably .... of the error. Make a slight change .... until the true setting is obtained ....

Figs. 35 and 36.—*Method of setting dividers* by calculation; line setting.

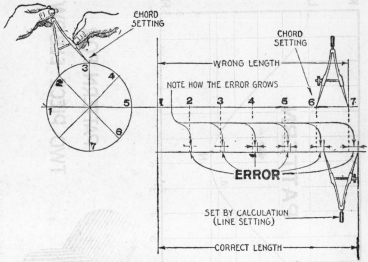

Fig. 37 and 38.—*Comparison of chord and line setting* of dividers showing magnitude of error due to its multiplication in spacing.

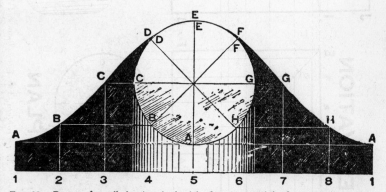

Fig. 39.—Pattern for cylinder (as obtained in figs. 31 to 33) in flat and rolled position showing its appearance in these positions.

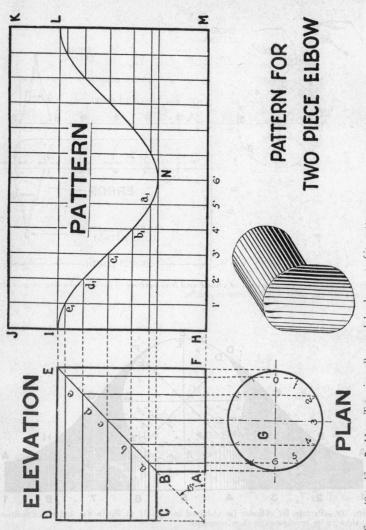

FIGS. 40 to 43.— *Problem.* Two piece elbow and development of its pattern.

CHAPTER 15

Development by Radial Lines

The second class of elementary surfaces are those whose elements are not parallel but radial from a common point.

Ques. What kind of objects have surfaces made up of radial lines?

Ans. Pyramids, cones, etc.

Ques. Name two subdivisions of radial line developments.

Ans. 1. Surfaces having three or more consecutive elements in the same plane. 2. Surfaces having no three consecutive elements in the same plane.

Ques. Give example of objects belonging to the first group.

Ans. Pyramids.

Ques. Give example of objects belonging to the second group.

Ans. Cones.

Examples of Radial Line Developments.—The following examples are given to illustrate the method of development by radial lines.

Example 1.—Development by radial lines of the pyramid shown in fig. 1.

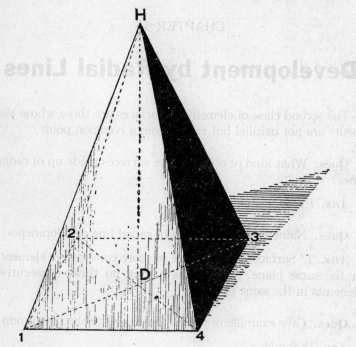

FIG. 1.—Pyramid in *cabinet projection*.

Ques. What should be drawn first?

Ans. An elevation and plan as shown in figs. 2 and 4.

Ques. What should be noted on examination of the pyramid?

Ans. It will be seen that the edges (H1, H2, H3, H4) are of equal length, and since these edges (which are elements of the surface) converge to a common point, their extremities in the development will lie in an arc of which the common point or apex is the center.

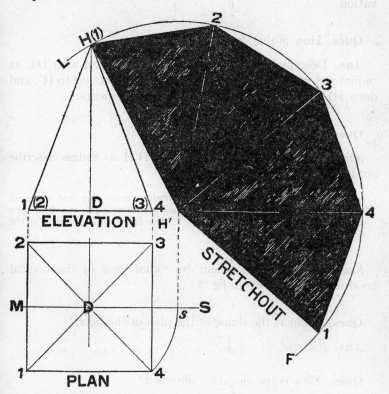

FIGS. 2 to 4.—*Development* by *radial lines* of the pyramid shown in fig. 1.

Ques. What should be noted about the elevation?

Ans. The elevation does not show the true length of the elements at the four corners.

Ques. What must be done to find the length of the elements?

Ans. Revolve one element as H4 into the plane of the elevation.

Ques. How is this done?

Ans. Describe an arc through point 4, in plan with D4, as radius and where this cuts axis MS, at s, project up to H', and draw HH', which gives true length of the elements.

Ques. How is the surface developed?

Ans. Take H' as center and with H'H as radius describe arc LF.

Set dividers to distance of one side obtained from plan and space off points 1, 2, 3, 4, 1 on LF. Connect these points with H', and draw lines connecting points 1, 2; 2, 3; 3, 4; 4, 1. The figure thus obtained is the developed surface of the pyramid.

Example 2.—Development by radial lines of the conical hood for a pipe shown in fig. 5.

Ques. What is the shape of the plan of the hood?

Ans. A circle.

Ques. How is the elevation obtained?

Ans. The elevation will be a triangle whose base equals diameter of the plan and whose altitude equals height of the cone, that is from base to apex.

Ques. How is the surface of the cone developed?

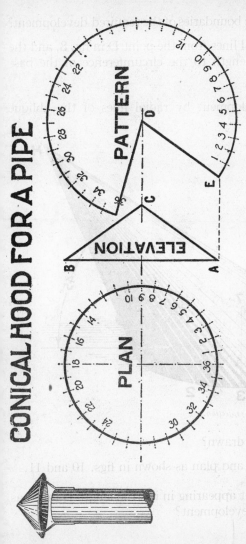

FIGS. 5 to 8.—Conical hood on a smoke stack and development of its surface.

Ans. Divide the base circle into any number of equal parts, say 36. Then, from any point D, as center, with the radius DE, equal to AC, that is equal to the oblique height of the cone, describe an arc upon which, starting at the point E, set off, in succession, all the parts into which the base circle is divided, in this case, 36 equal parts, so that the full length of the circumference of the base circle will be stretched out upon the arc.

Ques. What are the boundaries of the required development?

Ans. The two radial lines from the point D in fig. 8, and the arc that is equal in length to the circumference of the base circle of the cone.

Example 3.—Development by radial lines of the oblique cone shown in fig. 9.

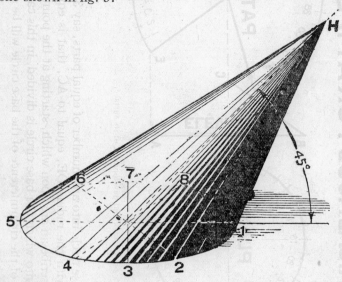

FIG. 9.—Oblique cone in *cabinet projection.*

Ques. What is first drawn?

Ans. The elevation and plan as shown in figs. 10 and 11.

Ques. What element appearing in its true length is taken as the beginning of the development?

Ans. H1, fig. 11.

Ques. Do the other elements appear in true length?

Ans. With exception of element H5, the others do not appear in true length.

Ques. Describe the various steps in developing the surface.

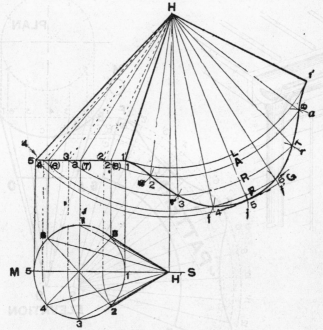

Figs. 10 and 11.—*Development* by *radial lines* of the oblique cone shown in fig. 9.

Ans. Revolve H'2, to MS, in plan and project up to 2' in elevation giving H2' as true length of H2.

Similarly obtain H3' and H4', true lengths of H3 and H4. With H, as center and radius H1, describe arc L; with radius H2', arc A; with radius H3', arc R; with radius H4', arc F; with radius H5, arc G. Set compasses to common distance between elements in plan as distance between points 1 and 2. With dividers set to this distance and with 1 (in stretch out) as center describe arc *a*, cutting A at 2; with 2, as center, arc *r*, cutting R, as center; with 3, as center, arc *f*, cutting F at 4; with 4, as center, arc *g*,

PATTERN FOR A CONICAL EAVE TROUGH OUTLET

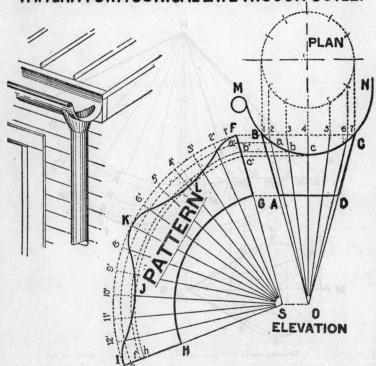

Figs. 12 to 15.—Conical eave trough outlet and development of its surface.

cutting G at 5. This gives points for half of the pattern of which the other half is similar, the points 6, 7 and 8, being obtained by the intersection of arcs *f'*, *r'*, *a'*, with F', R, A. Join all the points by a curve and draw 1'H, thus completing the pattern.

Example 4.—Development by radial lines of the conical eave trough outlet shown in fig. 12.

It does not matter what curve be given to the gutter, oval or circular. The method explained in this case is suitable for gutters of all curvatures.

> In this case the cross section of the gutter is represented at MBCN in elevation. The conical outlet which is to form a connecting piece between the gutter and the pipe, is a truncated cone whose wider end is shaped so as to conform with the surface of the gutter.

> The cone of which the connection piece is a part, is represented as BOC. The dotted line BC, represents the diameter of the base of this cone; the circumference of it being shown in plan.

Ques. Describe the method of development.

Ans. First develop the truncated cone ABCD, obtain the figure bounded by the radial lines HI, and GF (each equal to AB), and by the arc IKF and HG, the larger arc described with a radius equal to OB, while the smaller arc has a radius equal to OA.

Ques. What is the length of the larger arc?

Ans. It is equal to the sum of all the division on the circumference of the circle shown in the plan.

Ques. How are these divisions marked?

Ans. They are marked on the development by the points 1′2′3′, etc.

> The points 1, 2, 3, etc., on the base line BC, being connected with the vertex O, by straight lines, the surface of the cone appears with a series of elements or lines converging in the vertex. On the development of the cone, these elements appear as the radiating lines S1′, S2′, S3′, etc.

> Where the elements of the cone are intercepted by the cross section of the gutter, there are the points B, *a*, *b* and *c*, which are projected to the line

FG, by projectors parallel to BF, thus marking off on the line GF, the points F, *a'*, *b'* and *c'*. From these points, describe the arcs *a'e*, *b'f* and *c'h*. These arcs, in their intersections with the lines S1', S2', S3', etc., define the curved outward boundary FLKJI, of the required pattern.

Ques. What modification should be made in making an actual pattern for the trough outlet?

Ans. The pattern should be enlarged along the curved boundary by the addition of stock for laps or locks.

CHAPTER 16

Triangulation

There are some forms of elementary surfaces so shaped that although straight lines can be drawn on them, such lines when drawn would neither be parallel nor inclined toward each other with any degree of accuracy.

Ques. What kind of elements are not contained on such surfaces?

Ans. They contain neither parallel nor radial elements.

Ques. What can be drawn on such surfaces.

Ans. Two or more elements can be drawn in certain directions forming angles.

On such irregular surfaces it may happen that no two of the angles thus drawn on the solid, or represented, either correctly or foreshortened, in the projection drawing, will lie in the same plane or be equal to each other.

Since it is possible thus to project these angles, evidently they may be reproduced on the flat surface of the drawing paper in their correct size. If this can be done, it may be reasonably assumed that the surfaces thus represented will be the same as the corresponding surface of the solid surfaces belonging to the class and developed by the method of triangulation, and to the student who thoroughly understands the principles of projection, present no serious obstacles.

Ques. What are the steps in developing a surface by triangulation?

Ans. First the surface is divided up into a number of elementary triangles (hence the name *triangulation*). Next the true lengths of the sides of the triangles are found, and the triangles reproduced in the pattern.

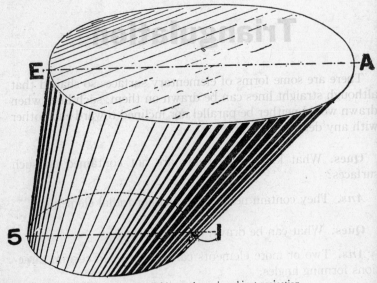

Fig. 1.—Irregular object with parallel bases shown in cabinet projection.

Example.—Development by triangulation of the irregular shaped object of fig. 1.

Ques. After drawing an elevation and plan as in figs. 2 and 4, what is the next step?

Ans. Select any number of points on the bottom edge and the same number of similarly located points on the top edge.

For simplicity only 8 points are taken on each edge (though in practice a greater number are taken).

Ques. How are the points similarly located?

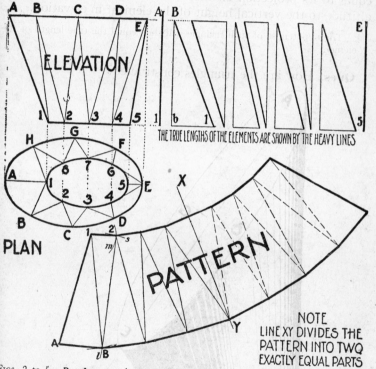

THE TRUE LENGTHS OF THE ELEMENTS ARE SHOWN BY THE HEAVY LINES

NOTE
LINE XY DIVIDES THE PATTERN INTO TWO EXACTLY EQUAL PARTS

FIGS. 2 to 5.—*Development* by *triangulation* of the irregular shaped object shown in fig. 1.

Ans. If points be taken for instance at the intersection of similar axes with the edges, they will be similarly located.

These points are 1, 3, 5, 7 for the bottom and A, C, E, and G for the top.

Ques. What is the next step?

Ans. Determine the true lengths of the elements by constructing for each element a right angle triangle whose base is equal to its projection on the base or length in plan, and its altitude to the vertical height of the element in elevation.

The hypotenuse of such triangle will then equal the true length of the element.

Ques. How are the triangles constructed?

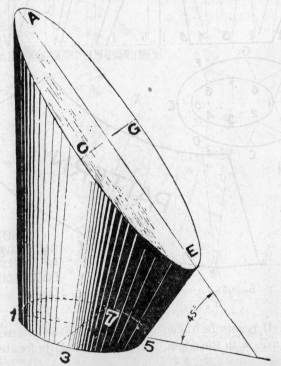

Fig. 6.—Irregular object with inclined top shown in *cabinet projection.*

Ans. Continue over to right the top and base in elevation and the distance between these lines will equal common altitude of the triangles. Beginning with element A1, its true length appears in elevation, hence it is not necessary to construct a triangle to find its true length.

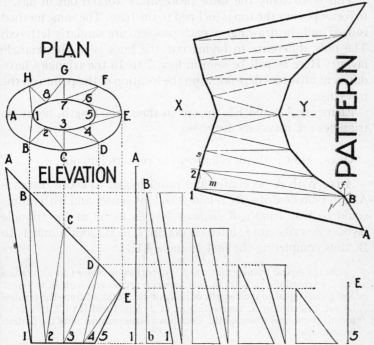

Figs. 7 to 18.—***Development*** by *triangulation* of the irregular shaped object shown in fig. 6.

For the next element B1, set dividers to distance B1, in plan, and mark this distance on base line of triangle layout as *b*1. Draw perpendicular *b*B, and join B1, thus completing the triangle. Its hypotenuse B1, then, is the true length of the element B1, which appears foreshortened in both plan and elevation.

In similar manner the true length of all the other elements are found. Next lay out the pattern, using the true lengths of the elements just found.

Example.—Development by triangulation of the irregular shaped object of fig. 6.

This is virtually the same problem as worked out in figs. 2 to 5 except that the top is inclined to the base. The same method is used and the drawings of each problem are similarly lettered. The only difference in laying out the lines is in the triangle layout. Here as will be seen in figs. 7 to 18 the triangles have different altitudes depending on the location of the points on the top edge.

Elements A1, and E5, appear in their true length, hence no triangles are necessary for these.

Ques. How is the development or pattern laid out?

Ans. With A, as center and radius equal to chord distance AB, in plan describe arc *l*, and with l, as center and with radius equal to true length of element B1, as found in the triangle layout, describe arc *f*, intersecting arc *l*, at B. Join A and 1, to B, thus completing the first triangle A1B.

For the second triangle take point 1, of pattern as center and with radius equal to chord distance 12, in plan, describe arc *m*, and with B, as center and radius equal to true length of element B2, obtained from the triangle layout, describe arc *s*, intersecting *m*, at 2. Join 1 and B to 2, thus completing the second triangle 1B2. Continue in same manner until the pattern is completed.

CHAPTER 17

Warped Surfaces

By definition, a warped surface is *one in which a straight edge may be placed in contact only at a point*.

It is not possible to develop a warped surface.

Ques. Why is it not possible to develop a warped surface?

Ans. Because the surface does not contain elements.

Ques. After developing a pattern approximating a warped surface what is necessary to be done to make the pattern coincide with the surface?

Ans. It is necessary to *raise* the surface of the metal pattern by hammering to shape so that when the pattern is in position it will fit.

Ques. Give a typical example of a warped surface.

Ans. A sphere.

Example.—Develop a pattern for the warped surface of a hemisphere or half sphere.

Ques. How is the warped surface divided?

Ans. It is divided into as many sections as desired.

The nearer will the pattern of each section approach to the shape of the warped surface when placed in position; that is, the less will be the amount of hammering necessary to *raise* the surface of the pattern so it will coincide with the warped surface.

Ques. In dividing the hemisphere into sections, of what do the sections consist?

Fig. 1.—Hemisphere shown in *cabinet projection*.

Ans. They may be either 1, zones, or 2, segments.

This gives rise to two developing methods, 1, zone method, and 2, segment method.

Case 1.—Zone Method.—In fig. 2, draw elevation of hemisphere and divide it into zones A, B, C.

Ques. What are the zones A and B?

Ans. Frustums of cones.

Ques. What is zone C?

Ans. A zone.

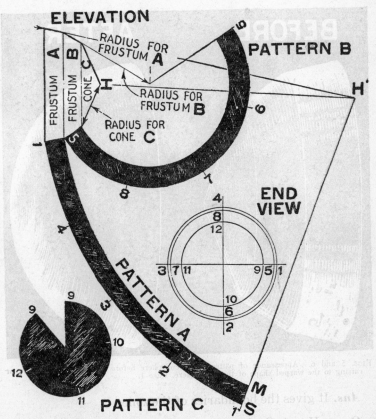

ELEVATION

RADIUS FOR FRUSTUM **A**

PATTERN B

FRUSTUM **A**

FRUSTUM **B**

CONE **C**

RADIUS FOR FRUSTUM **B**

RADIUS FOR CONE **C**

END VIEW

PATTERN A

PATTERN C

Figs. 2 to 4.—*Development* of hemisphere. *Case 1. Zone method.*

Ques. What is the first step in development of frustum A.?

Ans. Continue slant surface of frustum A, till it intersects the axis at H', giving radius center for frustum A. With H', as center describe the two arcs M and S.

Ques. What is the object of the end view?

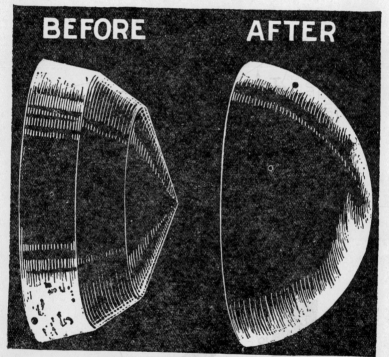

BEFORE   **AFTER**

Figs. 5 and 6.—Appearance of pattern for hemisphere before and after hammering or raising to the warped shape of the hemisphere. Case 1.

Ans. It gives the boundaries of the zones.

Ques. How is the length of the development obtained?

Ans. In end view rectify arc 12, and with this rectified arc length space off on arc S, the points 1, 2, 3, 4 and 1.

Ques. How is the pattern or development completed?

Ans. By connecting M and S, that is extending the radial line H'M to S.

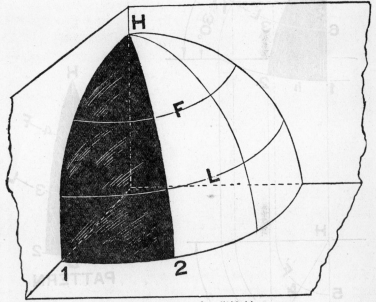

Fig. 7.—Quadrant of a hemisphere showing surface divided into segments.

Ques. How is frustum B and cone C developed?

Ans. In a similar manner as indicated in figs. 2 to 4.

Ques. What is the appearance of the three patterns when assembled?

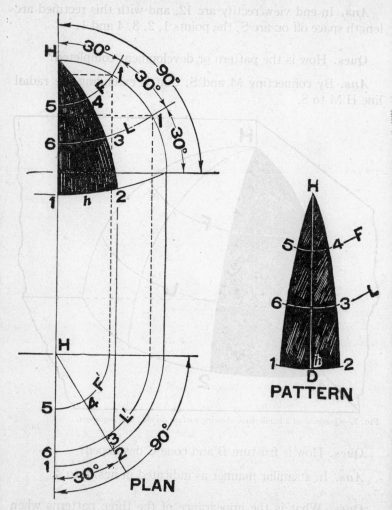

Ans. They appear as in fig. 5.

Ques. What must be done to bring the assembly to the shape of a hemisphere?

Ans. The metal of the patterns must be raised to the warped shape of the hemisphere by hammering.

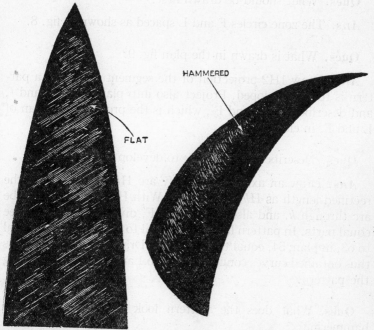

FLAT

HAMMERED

Figs. 11 and 12.—*Appearance of pattern* for hemisphere before and after hammering. *Case 2. Segment method.*

Case 2.—*Segment Method.*—Fig. 7 shows appearance of ¼ of the hemisphere which is divided into two segments. The shaded surface 1H2 being one of these sections. It is only necessary to develop a pattern for one section as all the others are of the same shape.

Ques. How does fig. 8 show the hemisphere?

Ans. Partly in cabinet projection and partly in elevation.

Ques. What should be drawn first?

Ans. The zone circles F and L spaced as shown in fig. 8.

Ques. What is drawn in the plan fig. 9?

Ans. Draw 1H2 projection of the segment for which a pattern is to be developed. Project also into plain points *l* and *f*, and describe zone L and F′, which is the projection in plan of L and F, in elevation.

Ques. Describe in detail how to develop the pattern.

Ans. Draw an axis HD. Rectify arc H*h*, and mark off the rectified length as H*h*, on pattern. With H as center, describe arc through *h*, and also arcs L and F, dividing H*h* into three equal parts. In pattern lay off 1 2 equal to 1 2 in plan; 63, equal to 63, in plan; 54, equal to 54 in plan. Draw through the points thus obtained curves connecting H, to 1 and 2, thus completing the pattern.

Ques. What does the pattern look like *before* and *after* hammering?

Ans. As in figs. 11 and 12.

Note in fig. 11 that the pattern *before* hammering is flat.

CHAPTER 18

Architectural Drawings

Architectural drawings are based on the same fundamental principles that have been explained in the preceding chapter with some specialized conventional representations and symbols.

That is to say, an architect's set of working drawings for a building, will consist of a number of plans, front and side elevations, sectional views, etc.—the same, based on orthographic projections as for machinists' drawings.

Ques. Just what do you understand by the expression "Architect's set of *plans*?"

Ans. A ridiculous misnomer and nothing can be done about it.

Ques. Why do they use such an expression?

Ans. It was ignorantly coined and survives by the power of suggestion.

Ques. Why is it a misnomer?

Ans. Because an architect's alleged "set of *plans*" consists of *elevations* as well as *plans*. In fact were it not for the elevations the house could not be built.

Architectural Practice.—To illustrate architectural drawings from the very beginning of a so-called set of plans to the finished drawings, consider first, the first interview between the architect and his client.

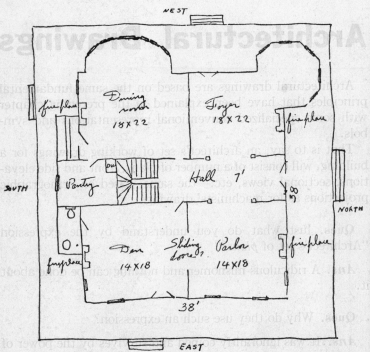

NEST

fire-place

Dining room
18 X 22

Foyer
18 X 22

fire-place

SOUTH

Pantry

Hall 7'

38

NORTH

Den
14 X 18

Sliding doors?

Parlor
14 X 18

fireplace

fireplace

38'

EAST

Fig. 1.—Owner's single line free hand sketch of proposed building. *First floor plan.*

Ques. What happens at the first interview?

Ans. The client has in mind the general arrangement of the house he wants and tries to convey his ideas to the architect by crude sketches such as shown in figs. 1 and 2.

It is for the architect to obtain from this and from questioning, a general idea of what is wanted. The sketch will serve as a memorandum and during the interview the architect will add a few principal dimensions, as given by client.

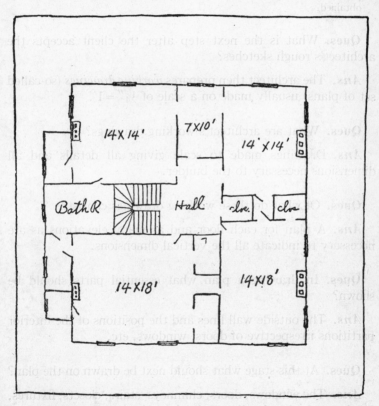

The preliminary sketches are then taken over and being rough, are easily altered until something satisfactory to the client is obtained.

Ques. What is the next step after the client accepts the architect's rough sketches?

Ans. The architect then prepares working drawings (so-called set of plans usually made on a scale of $\frac{1}{8}'' = 1$

Ques. What are architect's working drawings?

Ans. Drawings made to scale giving all details and all dimensions necessary to the builder.

Ques. On what is such a plan based?

Ans. A plan for each floor, and on this plan is shown the outline of rooms and it indicate all the critical dimensions.

Ques. In addition to a plan, what other part should be shown?

Ans. The outside wall lines and the positions of the interior partitions in perspective of doors windows, etc.

Ques. At this stage what should next be drawn on the plan?

Ans. The inside and outside outline of wall, doors, stairs,

Fig. 2.—Owner's single line free hand sketch of proposed building. *Second floor plan.*

From the information thus gained, the architect will prepare for the next interview a reproduction of the client's rough sketch drawn to say "⅛" scale," and add a perspective free-hand sketch giving an idea of the appearance of the building. The client can then get a better idea of how the building will look.

These preliminary sketches are then talked over, and being drawn in pencil, are easily altered until something satisfactory to the client is obtained.

Ques. What is the next step after the client accepts the architect's rough sketches?

Ans. The architect then prepares *working drawings* (so-called set of plans) usually made on a scale of $\frac{1}{4}'' = 1'$.

Ques. What are architect's working drawings?

Ans. Drawings made to scale giving all details and all dimensions necessary to the builder.

Ques. Of what do these working drawings consist?

Ans. A plan for each floor and as many elevations as are necessary to indicate all the vertical dimensions.

Ques. In drawing a plan what essential parts should be shown?

Ans. The outside wall lines and the positions of the interior partitions irrespective of doors, windows, etc.

Ques. At this stage what should next be drawn on the plan?

Ans. The windows, doors, chimneys, stairs, closets, fixtures, porches and other details may be shown in their correct location.

Ques. What should be noted in drawing plans and elevations?

Ans. Always work to center line of windows, doors and like details instead of working to the sides of them.

Ques. Why?

Ans. By this method the work may be done more rapidly.

As to Interior Arrangements.—The architect is always hampered in designing the interior by the suggestions of his client, which he must follow more or less.

Ques. What determines sizes of rooms and their location?

Ans. The requirements and the direction in which the building is to face. The service for which the room is intended and the furniture.

For instance the kitchen requires space for range, boiler, sink with drain board, table, etc.

Such details will not be considered here as after all this is a book on how to read blue prints—not how to build a house.

General Draughting Procedure.—With the small amount of data usually given by the client it can be readily seen that much depends on the ability of the architect to carry out his work rapidly and efficiently. He can only do this by having a thorough and broad understanding of the subject. Above all, he must follow a definite system of drawing, blocking out the important points first, and filling in details afterwards, as shown in the accompanying illustrations. This method is easier, quicker and more comprehensive than the method adopted by some student draughtsmen who early in the work labor over unimportant details, almost to the utter neglect of the more essential parts of the drawing.

In the accompanying illustrations, figs. 1 to 23, the student will proceed with the plans and elevations almost line for line the same as the professional draughtsman would do.

This method is used in working out all drawings whether for small or large buildings. The only differences are in the size,

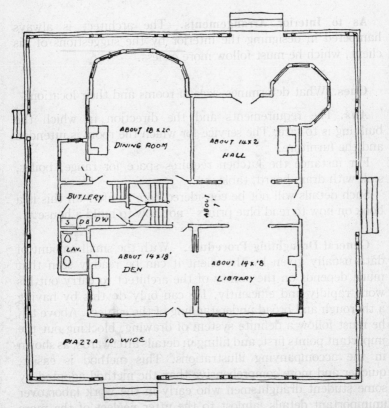

Fig. 3.—Architect's preliminary free hand sketch conforming to owner's ideas indicated in fig. 1. *First floor plan.*

the arrangement of the rooms, the location of partitions, etc.
All drawings should of course, be first carefully drawn in lead
pencil, and then just as carefully "inked in."

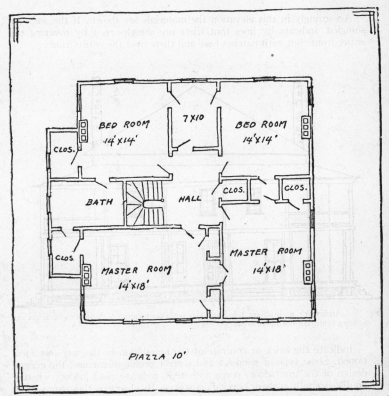

FIG. 4.—Architect's preliminary free hand sketch conforming to owner's ideas indicated in
fig. 2. *Second floor plan.*

Ques. What is the procedure with respect to elevations?

Ans. Usually each side of the house is shown.

Ques. Why is the front elevation made the most elaborate?

Ans. Because the owner wants especially to see how the building will look from the street.

Accordingly in this elevation the materials are shown. If the walls be shingled, indicate by lines that there are shingles, not by covering the entire front, but with patches here and there over the entire front.

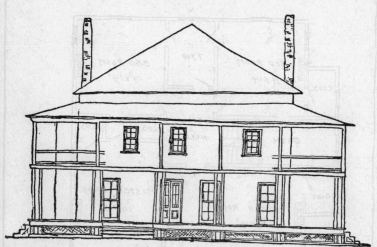

Fig. 5.—Architect's preliminary free hand elevation conforming with owner's sketches and showing tentative outline of roof.

Indicate the brick or concrete of the foundation in the way just mentioned. Show type of windows and correct profile of cornice; the general design of the front door, porch and steps; indicate glass in door whether double strength, plate or beveled plate glass. By observing these suggestions the owner can see at once just what materials are used and the general appearance of the building from the front.

Ques. How are the owner's free hand sketches made?

Ans. With single lines as in figs. 1 and 2.

With this rough sketch and list of requirements the architect is ready to make preliminary pencil sketches, which are subject to revision before the final drawings are begun.

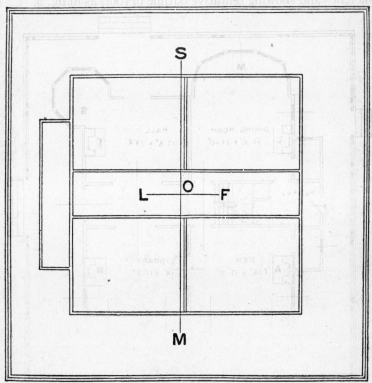

FIG. 6.—*Development 1* of plan of first floor.

Ques. How do the architect's free hand sketches differ?

Ans. They are two line sketches showing walls, windows, doors, partitions, etc., in more detail and appear as in figs. 3 and 4

Ques. What is the next drawing made by the architect?

Ans. A free hand elevation conforming with the owner's sketches and showing tentative outline of roof, as in fig. 5.

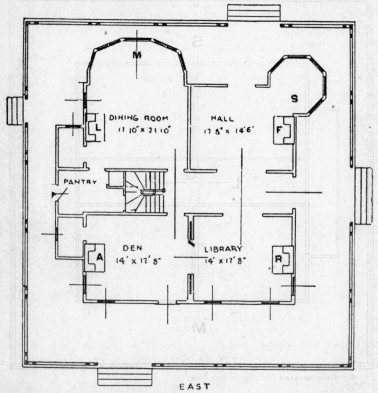

Fig. 7.—*Development 2* of plan of first floor.

Ques. How is the plan of first floor developed?

Ans. First draw main walls and partition showing them by two lines spaced to given thicknesses, as in fig. 6, extending them entire length irrespective of doors, etc. Similarly draw extension at the left, also piazza, showing thickness of rail.

Ques. Describe the final work in developing plan of first floor.

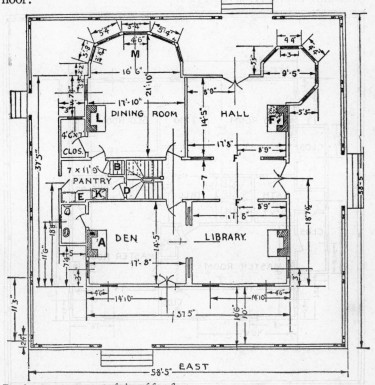

Fig. 8.—*Development 3* of plan of first floor.

Ans. When the plan has reached the stage shown in fig. 7, it is completed by sketching in all the details, of windows, doors, showing the way they swing, etc., and putting in all the dimensions necessary for the builder, indication of materials, etc., the drawing after this is done, having the appearance as in fig. 8. K, dumb waiter; B, cellar stairs; L,A,R,F, fire places; D, pantry to hall; EE, sink and drain board; F, portiere openings; G, sliding doors; H, lavatory.

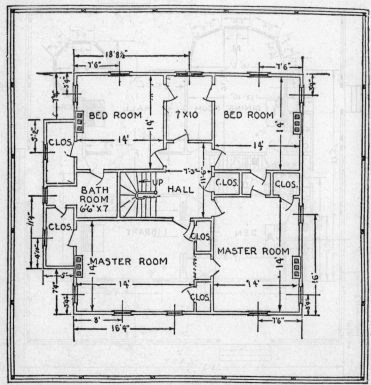

Fig. 9.—Finished plan of second story. This is drawn similarly as explained in figs. 6 to 8.

Ques. How is the plan of the second story drawn?

Ans. This is drawn in fig. 9, similarly as explained in figs. 6 to 8.

Ques. How is the east elevation started (Step 1)?

Ans. As in fig. 10. Here draw grade line and vertical axis through center of house as obtained from fig. 6, being there represented in plan as the inersection O, of MS with LF.

Ques. Describe Step 2, in developing east elevation?

Ans. In fig. 11 lay off at the side of the drawing the principal vertical dimensions A, B, C, D, E, F, G. These show distances between floors, depth of basement, height of first floor joists

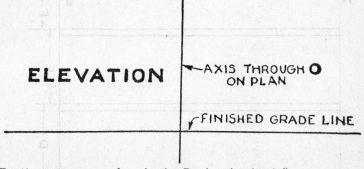

ELEVATION ←—AXIS THROUGH **O** ON PLAN

⌐FINISHED GRADE LINE

Fig. 10.—*Development 1* of east elevation. Drawing axis and grade line.

above grade line, and height of roof. Draw vertical lines HI, and JK, indicating sides of building and block in roof outline. Indicate space taken up by flooring joists and ceiling for each story by light horizontal parallel lines.

Note that the dimensions extend to the floor levels, hence draw ceiling lines below with the proper spacing.

Ques. Describe Step 3, in developing east elevation.

Ans. Transfer from plans figs. 8 and 9, measurements for vertical line of windows, doors, etc., by marking them off on a strip of paper and reproducing them in the elevation, fig. 12, by lines of indefinite length. Draw in the center lines lightly, as they will be found useful in working out the details of the windows and doors. Draw piazza floor and piazza roof lines.

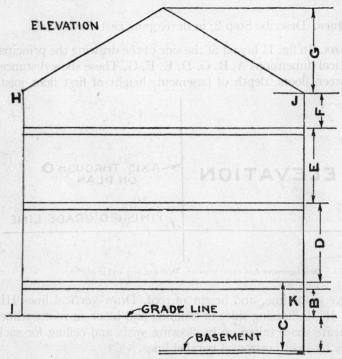

ELEVATION

Fig. 11.—*Development 2* of east elevation.

Ques. Describe Step 4 in developing east elevation.

Ans. Work up details of windows, door, piazza, railing steps, basement lattice work, etc. Indicate principal dimensions, construction notes, etc., thus completing the elevation.

Ques. How are the doors and windows shown?

Ans. By detail drawings such as in figs. 14 and 15.

To be complete these drawings should be fully dimensioned.

Ques. How is the piazza railing shown.

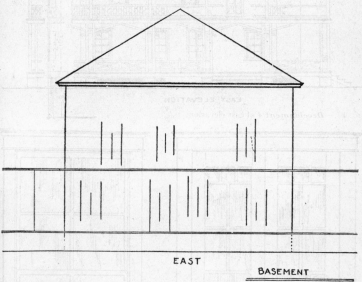

EAST

BASEMENT

FIG. 12.—*Development 3* of east elevation.

Ans. By a detail of one unit as in figs. 16 and 17.

Ques. Mention two other elevations.

Ans. Fig. 18 is an elevation showing foundation, sill, piazza beams and surrounding brick area under piazza; fig. 19, shows elevation detail of second floor ribband joist support.

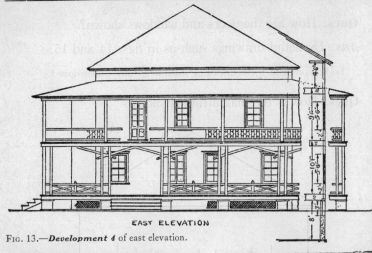

EAST ELEVATION

Fig. 13.—*Development 4* of east elevation.

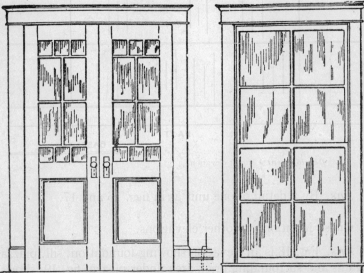

Fig. 14.—Detail of double door east side.

Fig. 15.—Detail of windows.

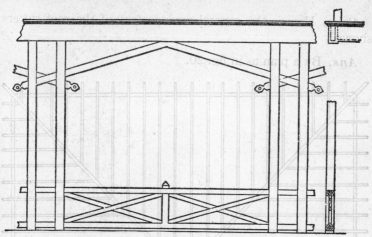

Figs. 16 and 17.—Side end view elevations, showing detail of piazza railing and column construction. *First floor.*

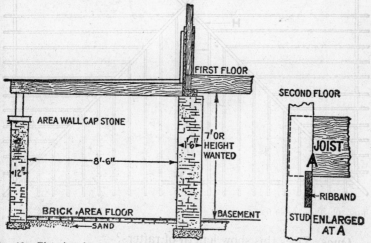

IG. 18.—Elevation showing foundation of sill piazza beams and surrounding brick area under piazza.

IG. 19.—Elevation showing second floor ribband joist support.

Ques. How is the general arrangement of the roof rafters shown?

Ans. By a plan as in fig. 20.

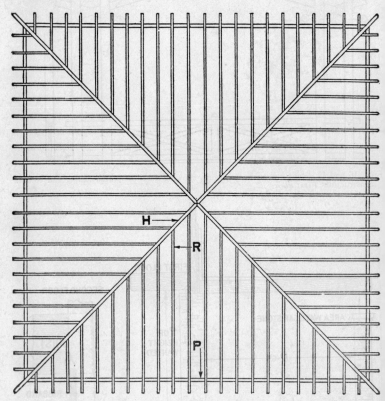

FIG. 20.—Plan of roof frame.

Ques. Does this show length of rafters?

Ans. No.

Ques. What data in addition to information on plan, is necessary to find length of rafters?

Ans. The *pitch* of the roof.

FIG. 21.—Elevation showing detail of cornice.

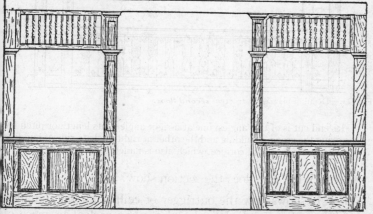

FIG. 22.—Interior woodwork in main hall.

Ques. In what drawing will be found more details of the roof construction?

Ans. In the detail elevation of the cornice as in fig. 21.

Ques. What does this detail show?

Ans. A strong simple method of construction. The rafters are notched over 4×4 plate.

Fig. 23.—Detail of piazza construction *second floor.*

Its end cut is of two angles, one at a right angle to its length or pitch for receiving the crown moulding and the other at right angle to side of building to receive the corona of cornice, which also is nailed to an outrigger.

Ques. What else does the section show?

Ans. It shows how the outrigger or ceiling furring is nailed to foot of rafter, and secured to house by a cleat or piece of furring being nailed to sheathing at the point necessary to align the whole to a level.

Ques. What do the vertical dotted lines through rafter to roof boards show?

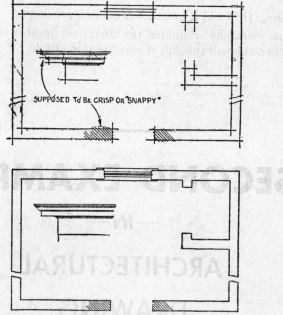

SUPPOSED TO BE CRISP OR "SNAPPY"

Figs. 24 and 25.—Comparison of the two styles of architectural drawings.

Ans. They show sheathing board cut in tight between rafters.

Ques. What is the object of these sheathing boards?

Ans. By reason of shrinkage of lumber leaving open joints, a large amount of cold air may be drawn into the house if this space be not closed, carrying cold air into the attic.

Crossing of Lines in Architectural Drawing.—This almost universal practice among architectural draughtsmen does not represent carelessness due to haste, but is a studied effort on the part of the draughtsmen to produce what they call a "crisp snappy" drawing.

Ques. How did it get such a hold on architects?

Ans. Someone originated the idea, then another imitated it, and then they all thought it was the thing to do.*

*NOTE.—The author fails to see anything "crisp" or "snappy" about this mode of drawing and does not recommend it. Also, it has the appearance of a method to employ cheap labor.

SECOND EXAMPLE

—*IN*—

ARCHITECTURAL

DRAWING

As a second example in architectural practice, the series of plates here presented illustrate the development of architectural drawings beginning with plans such as appear in magazines from time to time. This provides an excellent starting point and saves owner much time and study. They are equally appreciated by the builder for obvious reasons.

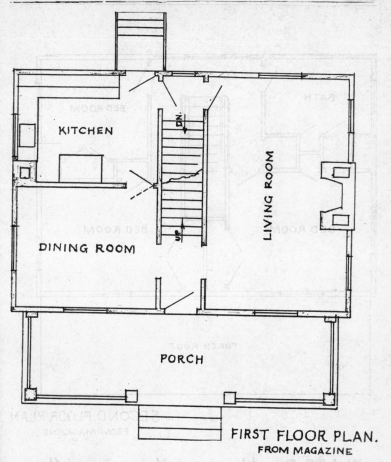

FIRST FLOOR PLAN.
FROM MAGAZINE

PLATE 1—*Magazine plan; first floor.*

Now let us assume that we shall start with the magazine plans shown in Plates 1 and 2. These two plans were prepared by a capable architect who has given us a practical and logical arrangement of plan,

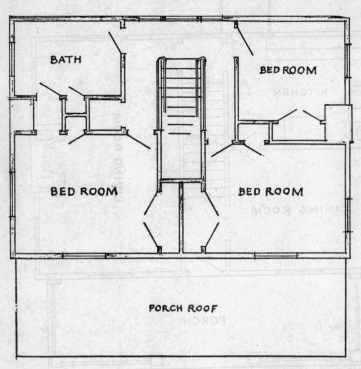

SECOND FLOOR PLAN.
FROM MAGAZINE

PLATE 2 — *Magazine plan; second floor.*

with stairs, doors, windows, closets, etc.; and indicated a proper and reasonable size of rooms. Any proposed changes or additions that the owner may desire, may be taken up with the architect or builder and easily whipped into form on his draughting board.

Conference with Builder.—Let us now assume that the owner prefers to deal only with a carpenter or builder of his acquaintance, and asks him to prepare the drawings and give him an estimate on construction. We will also assume that while the builder understands his own business from start to finish, that he does not pretend to be a good draughtsman and calls us in for advice on the preparation of the drawings. Having decided on the main features of the plans and elevations, we will start with the first floor plan of the house since that is always the controlling factor. Then, following the easy and usual method, we may trace the other plans (second floor and cellar) over it.

Changes Agreed Upon.—Upon a careful study of the first floor magazine plan, it is decided: first to place the large chimney and fireplace inside the house, against the stairs to conserve as much heat as possible since considerable heat is necessarily lost from an outside wall.

Next, omit kitchen chimney since a gas range is to be used. Third, move large porch to end of house since it provides more privacy; and change window to door, as indicated on **Plate 3**. Fourth, provide paved entrance platform with settee at front entrance. Fifth, coat closet at front entrance. Sixth, enlarged dining room, taking the space from the kitchen. Seventh, a first floor lavatory in small new wing at rear. These with other minor changes such as turning back steps, adding two small closets near fireplace, etc., substituting round for square porch columns, etc., creates a much more convenient and valuable first floor plan. The principle second floor change is one to save cost and involves a lowering of the front eaves line and cutting down size of front rooms as shown on **Plate 6**.

Draw in light lines (**Plate 3**) with an H or an F pencil, the outside walls and inside partitions without regard to openings (doors and windows) stairs, chimney, fireplace, closets, stoops, porches, or any other of the many details to be shown later. If we have not yet indicated the main center lines, they may be drawn in lightly now. This, then completes the first stage of the work. The outer walls to be drawn 7 ins. thick, room partitions 6 ins. thick and closet partitions 4 ins. thick.

Development of Working Drawings.—**Plates 3** to **6** drawn by Ives show various steps in the draughting work of completing the drawings **Plates 7** and **8** illustrate detail drawings for every operation that may present difficulty to the carpenter or mason.

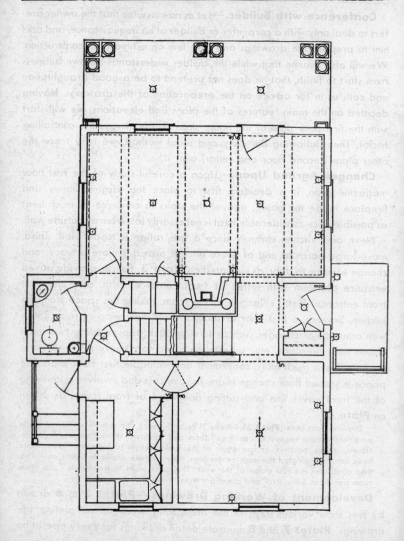

PLATE 3

Modified plan; first floor.

This plan is drawn in accordance with changes agreed upon after a discussion of the original magazine plan, **Plate 1**. In **Plate 3**, indicate all false ceiling beams, light fixtures, switches, outlets and push buttons, etc., and indicate the number of lights for each ceiling fixture.

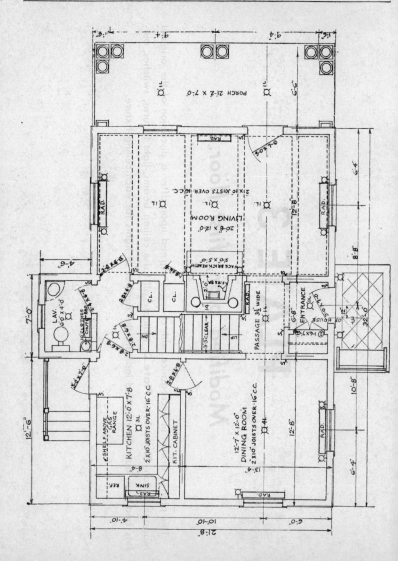

PLATE 4

Modified plan, first floor, dimensional drawing.

There are two general systems of dimensioning such plans as the house plan we are considering. One system is to centers of all openings and partitions and is probably the most rational and practical and the one least likely to lead to errors. In the layout of partitions especially it is the only reasonable method from the builder's standpoint. The other method is from surface to surface, which is very fine after the construction is completed, but involves much mental arithmetic and calculation on the part of the mechanic, with the ever present possibility of error. In laying out dimension and projection lines, the rules for same, already set forth, should be carefully followed.

In this plan draw in lightly, or in watered ink, all radiators or approximate sizes; also note sizes of all doors.

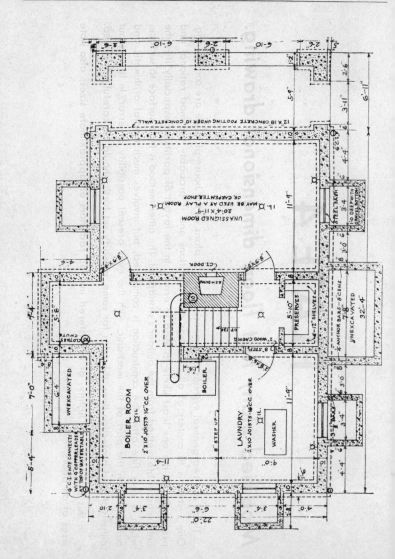

PLATE 5

Complete cellar plan.

This plan is developed by the various stages described for first floor. Note the concrete footing shown in dotted lines. The trouble with most foundation footings is the ridiculous penny wise saving idea of the owner in not allowing the builder to put in a footing large enough to carry the load without eventual settling. In some cases a footing twice the size recommended by the contractor, would not be unnecessarily large — especially in the case of competitive bidding.

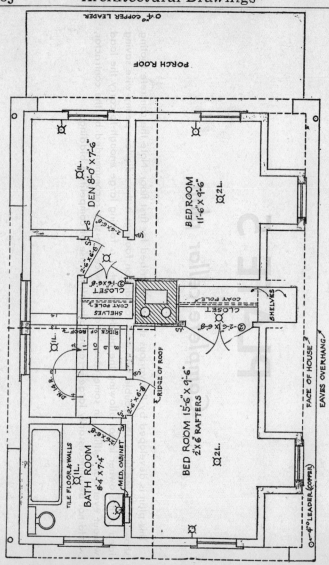

PLATE 6

Modified plan; second floor.

The outline of the walls is obtained from first floor plan. Here positions of the electric outlets and number of lights are shown, also the plumbing fixtures. Various dimensions are given such as for rooms, doors, etc.

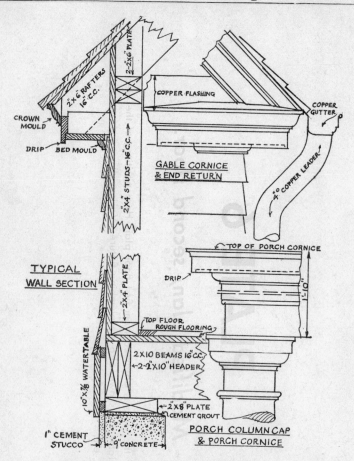

GABLE CORNICE & END RETURN

CROWN MOULD

DRIP   BED MOULD

2"x 6" RAFTERS 16" C.C.

2"-2"x6" PLATE

COPPER FLASHING

COPPER GUTTER

2"x4" STUDS-16" C.C.

4" COPPER LEADER

TYPICAL WALL SECTION

2"x4" PLATE

TOP FLOOR

ROUGH FLOORING

10"x 7/8" WATERTABLE

2 X 10 BEAMS 16"C.C.

2-2"x10" HEADER

2"x 8" PLATE

CEMENT GROUT

1" CEMENT STUCCO

9" CONCRETE

TOP OF PORCH CORNICE

DRIP

PORCH COLUMN CAP & PORCH CORNICE

PLATE 7 — Detail drawing

These details show a section through outside wall at floor and roof levels; also elevations of roof gable mouldings, porch column cap and cornice mouldings.

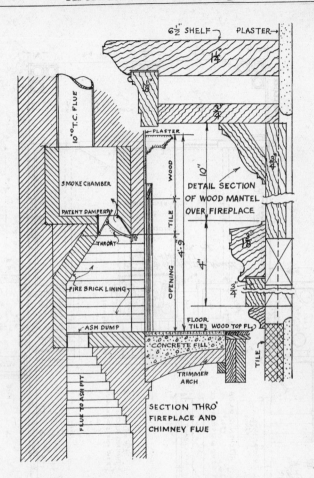

PLATE 8 — *Detail drawing.*

These details show section through living room, fireplace and larger detail section of wood mantel mouldings for same.

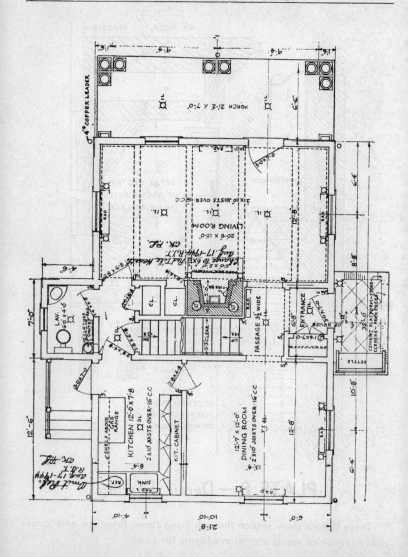

PLATE 9

First floor plan, indicating changes.

When a builder is preparing drawings for an owner, it should be definitely borne in mind that the owner invariably has a short memory and that whatever he has agreed to should be recorded in black and white, dated and signed, for future reference, so that later on, when he has forgotten all about it and declares that he never heard of it before, you may bring out the signed drawing (blue print) to refresh his memory. For this purpose a paper tracing should be prepared in soft pencil showing all changes in original plan ordered by owner.

Each change should then be O.K.'d, signed and dated by owner, and blue printed as a record. This may save the builder hundreds of dollars for changes which, without aforesaid blue print record, could be denied by owner who could sue the builder for not carrying out the plans according to contract. This happens so often that it is the rule rather than the exception in the building business.

Mill Made Doors.—Stock sizes of doors cover a wide range but those most commonly used are,

$$2'\ 6'' \times 6'\ 6''$$
$$2'\ 8'' \times 6'\ 8''$$
$$2'\ 10'' \times 6'\ 10''$$
$$3'\ \ \times 7'$$

These sizes either 1 ⅜ or 1 ¾ inches thick.

Single Inside Door Jambs.—On architects' plans figures for doors are generally given so that it will be easy to get the sizes.

For example, to measure or copy: commence by listing all the different widths of doors, say, 2' 4'', 2' 6'', and 3' 0''. Then take the different heights, as, 6' 6'', 6' 8'', 6' 10'', etc., as may be shown on plans, and make a list as on page 203.

Sizes of Four Light Sash

Size of Glass	Size of Window	Size of Glass	Size of Window
10'' × 20''	2' 1'' × 3' 10''	14'' × 26''	2' 9'' × 4' 10''
10'' × 22''	2' 1'' × 4' 2''	14'' × 28''	2' 9'' × 5' 2''
10'' × 24''	2' 1'' × 4' 6''	14'' × 30''	2' 9'' × 5' 6''
10'' × 26''	2' 1'' × 4' 10''	14'' × 32''	2' 9'' × 5' 10''
10'' × 28''	2' 1'' × 5' 2''	14'' × 34''	2' 9'' × 6' 2''
10'' × 30''	2' 1'' × 5' 6''	14'' × 36''	2' 9'' × 6' 6''
10'' × 32''	2' 1'' × 5' 10''	14'' × 38''	2' 9'' × 6' 10''
10'' × 34''	2' 1'' × 6' 2''	14'' × 40''	2' 9'' × 7' 2''
10'' × 36''	2' 1'' × 6' 6''	14'' × 42''	2' 9'' × 7' 6''
12'' × 20''	2' 5'' × 3' 10''	14'' × 44''	2' 9'' × 7' 10''
12'' × 22''	2' 5'' × 4' 2''	14'' × 46''	2' 9'' × 8' 2''
12'' × 24''	2' 5'' × 4' 6''	14'' × 48''	2' 9'' × 8' 6''
12'' × 26''	2' 5'' × 4' 10''	15'' × 24''	2' 11'' × 4' 6''
12'' × 28''	2' 5'' × 5' 2''	15'' × 26''	2' 11'' × 4' 10''
12'' × 30''	2' 5'' × 5' 6''	15'' × 28''	2' 11'' × 5' 2''
12'' × 32''	2' 5'' × 5' 10''	15'' × 30''	2' 11'' × 5' 6''
12'' × 34''	2' 5'' × 6' 2''	15'' × 32''	2' 11'' × 5' 10''
12'' × 36''	2' 5'' × 6' 6''	15'' × 34''	2' 11'' × 6' 2''
12'' × 38''	2' 5'' × 6' 10''	15'' × 36''	2' 11'' × 6' 6''
12'' × 40''	2' 5'' × 7' 2''	15'' × 38''	2' 11'' × 6' 10''
12'' × 42''	2' 5'' × 7' 6''	15'' × 40''	2' 11'' × 7' 2''
12'' × 44''	2' 5'' × 7' 10''	15'' × 42''	2' 11'' × 7' 6''
12'' × 46''	2' 5'' × 8' 2''	15'' × 44''	2' 11'' × 7' 10''
12'' × 48''	2' 5'' × 8' 6''	15'' × 46''	2' 11'' × 8' 2''
14'' × 14''	2' 9'' × 4' 6''	15'' × 48''	2' 11'' × 8' 6''

CHAPTER 19

Architect's Specifications

Ques. Are architects so-called set of "plans" all that is necessary for the contractor to construct the building?

Ans. No.

Ques. Why?

Ans. The architect's set of alleged "plans," that is, *working drawings* show completely the outline of the building and all the necessary general dimensions, but not a very considerable amount of data necessary to completely define the building in every respect.

Ques. What is missing in the working drawings?

Ans. The specifications.

Ques. What are specifications?

Ans. By definition a specification is *a definite, particularized and complete statement, setting forth the nature and construction of a detail of the thing to which it relates*, and as applied to building, **specifications** *describe briefly, yet eaxctly, each item in a list of the things required to complete an architectural contract.*

Ques. Why are specifications not put in by the draughtsman on the working drawings?

Ans. To add to the drawings all of the considerable data relating to the various materials, sizes of the wooden members, technique and conditions of the contract, would fill the drawings to such an extent as to more or less obscure the outline and leading dimensions of the building.

Ques. What precaution should be used in writing specifications to avoid misunderstandings and disputes?

Ans. Each item entering into the construction should be defined and described with such precision that there can be no chance of misunderstanding or double interpretation.

Ques. In writing specifications what should be avoided?

Ans. Any layman should not attempt to write them.

Ques. Why?

Ans. Why go to court without a lawyer?

For the guidance of architects in writing specifications the American Institute of Architects has prepared a number of "Standard Documents," and these should be carefully studied and consulted by the architect in writing specifications.

Standard Specifications.—Standard documents have been prepared by the American Institute of Architects and they should be used to avoid misunderstanding and disputes which would probably result in cases where laymen think they can improve on these documents which have been prepared after long study.

CHAPTER 20

Architects' Conventions

Although drawings whether for machinists or builders are based on the same fundamentals, they have characteristic differences as to conventional representations and symbols.

Frequently architectural drawings are not fully dimensioned with result that they have to be "scaled" by the workman. This is not supposed to happen on blue prints for machinists, but in such case the original drawing should be scaled and not the blue print.

The architectural conventions and symbols used by architects cover several fields of construction, as

1. Building details
2. Plumbing
3. Piping
4. Welding
5. Electrical

Building Conventions.—Walls of frame buildings are represented on floor plans by two parallel lines spaced at a distance apart equal to the wall thickness as at **A** in figs. 1 to 15.

Ques. How are masonry walls shown on a floor plan?

Ans. By cross sectional parallel lines as at **B**.

CONVENTIONS 1

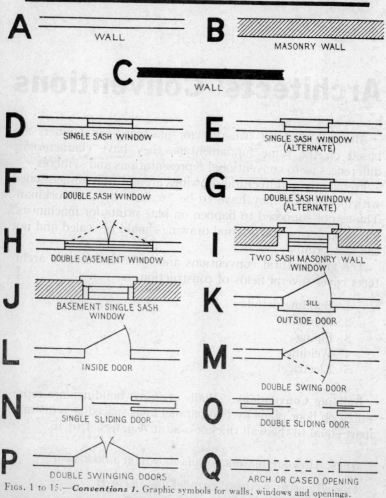

A — WALL

B — MASONRY WALL

C — WALL

D — SINGLE SASH WINDOW

E — SINGLE SASH WINDOW (ALTERNATE)

F — DOUBLE SASH WINDOW

G — DOUBLE SASH WINDOW (ALTERNATE)

H — DOUBLE CASEMENT WINDOW

I — TWO SASH MASONRY WALL WINDOW

J — BASEMENT SINGLE SASH WINDOW

K — SILL — OUTSIDE DOOR

L — INSIDE DOOR

M — DOUBLE SWING DOOR

N — SINGLE SLIDING DOOR

O — DOUBLE SLIDING DOOR

P — DOUBLE SWINGING DOORS

Q — ARCH OR CASED OPENING

FIGS. 1 to 15.—**Conventions 1**. Graphic symbols for walls, windows and openings.

Ques. What other method is used for representing walls?

Ans. Sometimes by filling in solid black between the wall lines as at **C**.

This saves time in draughting especially in the case of floor plans of large apartment houses having many rooms. It shows up the walls better and on photographic reductions avoids the "muddy" appearance of the reduced cross section lines.

Ques. How are windows represented?

Ans. In several ways depending upon the type.

In the illustrations (figs. 1 to 15) **D,** shows single sash window; **F,** double sash window; **H,** double casement window, etc.

The half hearted attempt to show these window conventions more pictorial as in the alternate methods **E** and **G,** are not recommended, as being a waste of time.

Ques. How are doors shown?

Ans. In various ways depending upon type as at **K, L, M, N, O.**

Ques. What is the alternate method of drawing the arcs of swinging doors?

Ans. They are often drawn dotted instead of solid.

Ques. What precautions should be taken as to reading architect's conventions for windows?

Ans. Windows are sometimes drawn with one line representing a sash and sometimes with two; accordingly, it is not always clear whether a double line represents a single or double sash.

Ques. What is the practice with respect to the line representing the sill edge?

Ans. It is not always shown on frame building drawings, but always on drawings for masonry buildings.

Ques. What is a peculiarity about the architect's use of dotted lines on floor plans?

CONVENTIONS 2

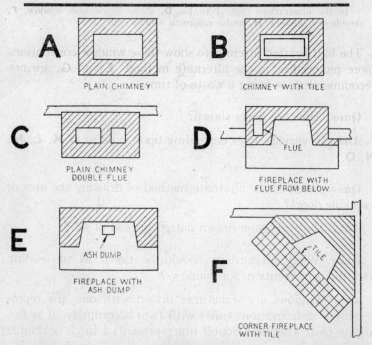

A PLAIN CHIMNEY

B CHIMNEY WITH TILE

C PLAIN CHIMNEY DOUBLE FLUE

D FIREPLACE WITH FLUE FROM BELOW — FLUE

E FIREPLACE WITH ASH DUMP — ASH DUMP

F CORNER FIREPLACE WITH TILE — TILE

Figs. 16 to 21.—*Conventions 2.* Graphic symbols for chimneys and fireplaces.

CONVENTIONS 3

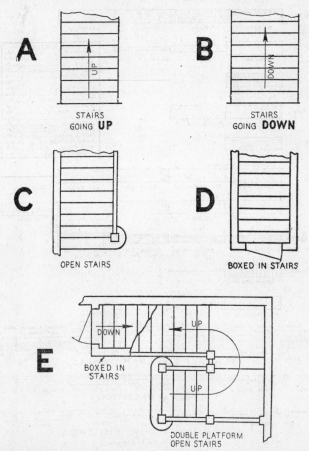

Figs. 22 to 26.—*Conventions 3.* Graphic symbols for stairs.

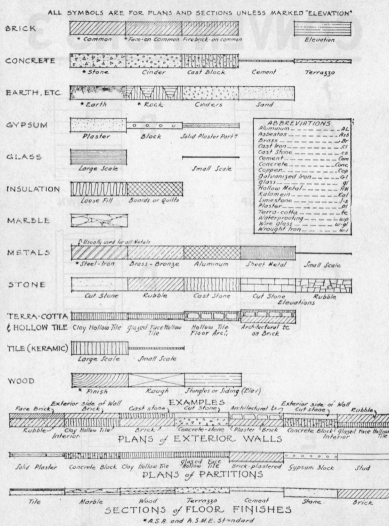

ALL SYMBOLS ARE FOR PLANS AND SECTIONS UNLESS MARKED "ELEVATION"

BRICK — * Common — * Face-on Common — Firebrick-on common — Elevation

CONCRETE — * Stone — Cinder — Cast Block — Cement — Terrazzo

EARTH, ETC. — * Earth — * Rock — Cinders — Sand

GYPSUM — Plaster — Block — Solid Plaster Part?

GLASS — Large Scale — Small Scale

INSULATION — Loose Fill — Boards or Quilts

MARBLE

METALS — *Usually used for all Metals* — * Steel-Iron — Brass-Bronze — Aluminum — Sheet Metal — Small Scale

STONE — Cut Stone — Rubble — Cast Stone — Cut Stone — Rubble / Elevations

TERRA-COTTA & HOLLOW TILE — Clay Hollow Tile — Glazed Face Hollow Tile — Hollow Tile Floor Arch — Architectural tc on Brick

TILE (KERAMIC) — Large Scale — Small Scale

WOOD — * Finish — Rough — Shingles or Siding (Elev)

ABBREVIATIONS	
Aluminum	AL
Asbestos	Asb
Brass	Br
Cast Iron	c-i
Cast Stone	cs
Cement	Cem
Concrete	Conc
Copper	Cop
Galvanized Iron	Gl
Glass	gl
Hollow Metal	HM
Kalamein	Kal
Limestone	l-s
Plaster	Pl
Terra-cotta	tc
Waterproofing	wp
Wire glass	w-gl
Wrought Iron	w-i

EXAMPLES

Face Brick — Exterior side of Wall / Brick — Cast stone — Cut Stone — Architectural tc — Exterior side of Wall / Cut stone — Rubble

Rubble — Clay Hollow Tile / Interior — Brick — Concrete-stone — Plaster / Brick — Concrete Block / Interior — Glazed face Hollow Tile

PLANS of EXTERIOR WALLS

Solid Plaster — Concrete Block — Clay Hollow Tile — Glazed face Hollow Tile — Brick-plastered — Gypsum Block — Stud

PLANS of PARTITIONS

Tile — Marble — Wood — Terrazzo — Cement — Stone — Brick

SECTIONS of FLOOR FINISHES

*A.S.A. and A.S.M.E. Standard

FIGS. 27 to 42.—**Conventions 4.** Graphic symbols of various materials.

Ans. They do not always show something below and hidden by the floor (as they should) but frequently they refer to something above the floor.

An example of this abuse of conventional lines is the convention at **Q**, for an arched or cased opening.

Ques. How are chimneys shown?

Ans. By sections, as illustrated in **CONVENTIONS 2**, figs. 16 to 21.

Note representations for plain and tiled chimenys **A** and **B**; flue and ash dump **D** and **E**, etc.

Ques. On a floor plan how is it known whether the stairs lead to the story above or below?

Ans. By an arrow marked "up" or "down" as in figs. 22 and 23. (**A** and **B**.)

Ques. What other conventions are used with respect to stairs?

Ans. The type of stairs is indicated as at **C**, **D** and **E**. (**CONVENTIONS 3**, figs. 24 to 26.)

Miscellaneous Conventions.—The foregoing graphical symbols or conventions are those relating to the building proper. In addition to these there are various groups necessary on draw-ings showing the several installations of equipment necessary for the completed building. The following graphical symbols in the several groups relate to:

1. Plumbing
2. Piping
3. Pipe fitting and valves
4. Heating and ventilating
5. Duct work

6. Heat power apparatus
7. Conventional rivets
8. Refrigerating
9. Welding
10. Electric power and wiring

All these graphic symbols have been standardized by the American Societies of Mechanical and Electrical Engineers and with special permission from these Societies the author is here able to give them in their entirety as they appear in the Codes published by the Societies. See pages 145 to 169.

CHAPTER 21

Boat Builders' Blue Prints

The shape of a hull is represented by a multiplicity of lines (straight and curved) consisting of several series: longitudinal, traverse, horizontal and vertical.

Marine or naval architects who design boats for boat builders have the same fault as house architects of calling everything on a blue print a *plan*, regardless of whether it be a *plan* or *elevation*. Such abuse of the word *plan* is very objectionable, especially by highly educated men such as naval architects. However, nothing can be done about it—not a thing, except to protest against the practice.

The working drawings or "lines" necessary for the boat builder consist of an assembly of orthographic views, known as:

1. So-called *sheer plan*
2. *Half breadth plan*
3. *Alleged body plan*

Figs. 1 to 3 show these three views giving the names by which they are generally known and key titles or properly applied names.

Ques. Why is the term sheer plan a misnomer?

Ans. It is a longitudinal elevation and should be so called.*

---

*NOTE.—Regardless of the argument probably dating back to Noah's Ark and often advanced in barber shops, saloons and other nondescript waterfront places that the so-called *sheer plan* lines are laid down full size on the horizontal floor of the shop; they are drawn on a horizontal drawing board for that matter but that does not make the drawing a *plan*.

Ques. What is the half breadth plan?

Ans. A real plan, looking down on the drawing which shows a longitudinal half view of the lines.

Ques. Why a half and not a whole breadth plan?

Ans. Since the longitudinal center line divides the hull into two symmetrical halves it is only necessary to show a half view.

SO CALLED SHEER PLAN
(LONGITUDINAL ELEVATION)

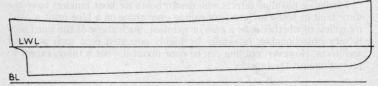

HALF BREADTH PLAN

ALLEGED BODY PLAN
TRANSVERSE OR BODY ELEVATION

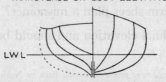

FIGS. 1 to 3.—The three views, *two elevations* and *a plan* which are the views necessary to completely show the "lines" of a boat.

Nomenclature.—Regardless of what marine architects call their drawings the author will call them by their right names, viz.:

1. Sheer elevation (longitudinal)
2. Body elevation (transverse)
3. Half breadth plan

Remembering that the sheer elevation is a longitudinal elevation (profile) and that the body elevation is a transverse elevation, there need not be any confusion as to these terms.

Ques. What is the alleged body plan?

Ans. Cross or transverse elevation showing the transverse shape of the hull at various points or "stations" along its length.

The Lines.—The numerous lines appearing on the working drawings of a hull consist of:

1. Water lines
2. Base line
3. Station lines or stations
4. Sheer line
5. Rabbet lines
6. Bearding lines
7. Bow lines
8. Buttocks
9. Diagonals

Water Lines.—These are horizontal lines, one of which is known as the *load water line* abbreviated L.W.L. On each side of this line, that is above and below, and parallel with it are several other lines known as water lines above, and water lines below abbreviated: W.L.1A, W.L.2A, etc., and W.L.1B, W.L.2B, etc. They are arranged in the drawing as shown in fig. 4.

Ques. In what other way are the various water lines indicated?

Ans. As WL1 up, WL2 up, etc., and WL1 down WL2, down, etc.

Sometimes they are indicated by their vertical dimensions and the letters U or D corresponding to up and down. Thus 1'-6" U, 3'U, etc. 1'-6" D, 3'D, etc.

Ques. What is the object of the load water line?

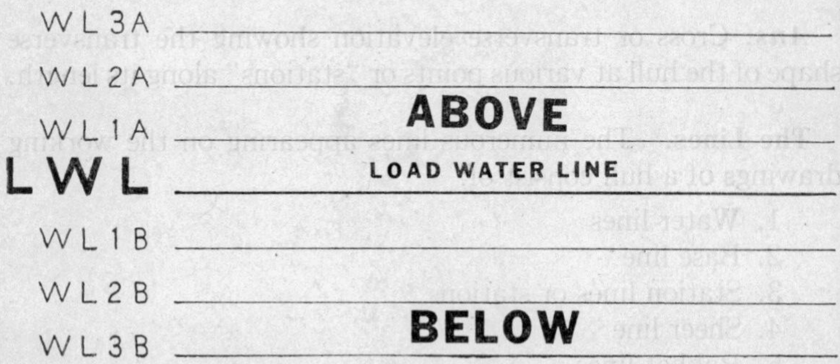

WL 3A _____

WL 2A _____

WL 1A _____ **ABOVE**

L W L _____ **LOAD WATER LINE**

WL 1B _____

WL 2B _____

WL 3B _____ **BELOW**

FIG. 4.—Method of numbering water lines.

Ans. It is the origin for all vertical measurements when they are not referred to the base line and represents the "water line" of the boat when fully loaded.

Ques. Name two kinds of water lines.

Ans. Straight and curved.

Ques. Where do the straight water lines appear?

Ans. In the sheer elevation.

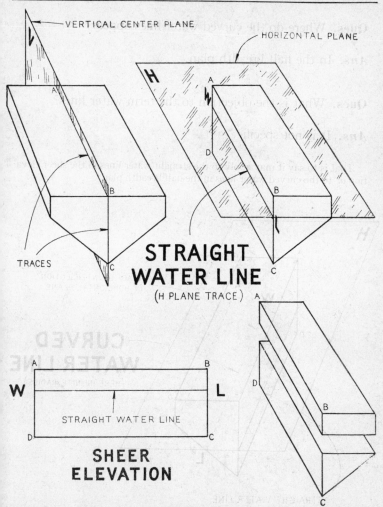

STRAIGHT WATER LINE

(H PLANE TRACE)

VERTICAL CENTER PLANE

HORIZONTAL PLANE

TRACES

SHEER ELEVATION

STRAIGHT WATER LINE

FIGS. 5 to 8.—Scow like block model used for simplicity for preliminary explanations of basic principles. Fig. 5, block with vertical plane V passing through center showing traces; fig. 6, half block with horizontal plane H, cutting block transversely into two parts (fig. 8) and fig. 7, *sheer elevation* of the half block.

Ques. Where do the curved water lines appear?

Ans. In the half breadth plan.

Ques. What is the objection to the term water lines?

Ans. It is not specific.

That is to say it may apply to the straight water lines in the sheer elevation or to the curved water lines in the half breadth plan.

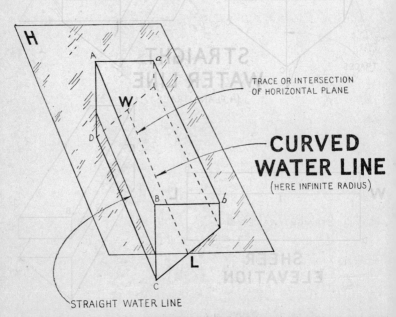

FIG. 9.—Half block cut by horizontal plane illustrating curved water line (seen in half breadth plan), so-called here to distinguish from the straight water lines which appear in the sheer elevation.

Ques. In reality just what is a straight water line?

Ans. The line (or trace) of intersection of a horizontal plane with the perpendicular longitudinal central plane.

To illustrate consider a scow-like block model of rectangular cross section above **L.W.L.** and triangular section below as shown in fig. 5. Now a vertical plane (**V**) passing through the center would cut the model along the lines AB and BC. These lines are "traces" of the intersection. Suppose the block be sawed in half through this intersection.

Remove one half and the other half would appear as in fig. 6. Pass a horizontal plane (**H**) through the model, at any elevation say as shown in fig. 6. This will intersect the block along the line **W.L.** This line then is one of the straight water lines which appear in the sheer elevation, and is shown as would be drawn in fig. 7. If the block were sawed along the **H** plane of

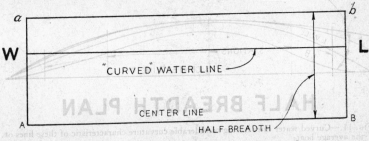

HALF BREADTH PLAN

FIG. 10.—*Half breadth plan* showing the curved water line **W.L.** seen pictorially in fig. 8.

fig. 6, the two parts would appear as in fig. 8. The drawings, figs. 5 to 8 are lettered to correspond.

Ques. In reality just what is a curved water line?

Ans. The curve (or trace) of intersection of a horizontal plane with a hull or side of a boat.

To illustrate consider the same block cut in half as in fig. 9. Pass a horizontal plane **H**, through the block at any elevation, say as shown in fig. 9.

This will intersect the block along the line **W.L.** This line then is one of the "curved" water lines which appear in the half breadth plan and is shown as it would be drawn in fig. 10. Note in fig. 10 the lettering is the same as in fig. 9.

Ques. Why is the water line shown in figs. 9 and 10 called curved?

Ans. This is the limiting case of a curved line, that is, it may

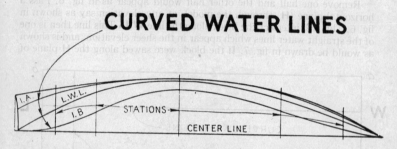

CURVED WATER LINES

HALF BREADTH PLAN

Fig. 11.—Curved water lines having considerable curvature characteristic of these lines of the average boat.

be regarded as a curve having an infinitely long radius which means a radius without end.

Unfortunately this limiting case was encountered because of the shape of the model block which was selected for simplicity in the preliminary explanations. In actual boat lines, the curved water lines are "very much curved" that is they don't look like straight lines as in figs. 9 and 10. For example observe the "very much curved" water lines in fig. 11.

Base Line.—The base line is a line of reference for all vertical measurements and it is generally used instead of the load water line.

Ques. Where is it located?

Ans. It is drawn parallel with the load water line and at a distance below the **L.W.L.** equal to or greater than the draught of the hull.

Ques. When is the distance between the **L.W.L.** and base line greater than the draught?

Ans. When it is desired to place the half breadth plan under the sheer elevation, and above the base line instead of on a separate drawing.

In fig. 12 position 2 of the base line shows this arrangement. Note space above base line for half breadth plan.

Ques. What other position is sometimes given to the base line?

Ans. It is sometimes located at position 1 (fig. 12) between the sheer elevation and half breadth plan.

Ques. What other measurements beside vertical measurements are laid off on the base line?

Ans. The station positions and diagonal intersections.

Stations.—By definition a station is *an axis drawn perpendicular to the base line and spaced at a definite distance from a given point to locate the position of a frame.*

Ques. What is a frame?

Ans. A template or mould corresponding to the cross sectional shape of the hull at a given station.

Ques. How are the stations spaced?

Ans. The load water line length of the hull is divided into an appropriate number of equal parts and perpendiculars erected at each division representing stations.

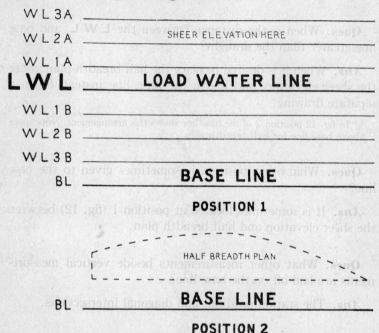

WL 3A

WL 2A   SHEER ELEVATION HERE

WL 1A

LWL   **LOAD WATER LINE**

WL 1B

WL 2B

WL 3B

BL   **BASE LINE**

POSITION 1

HALF BREADTH PLAN

BL   **BASE LINE**

POSITION 2

Fig. 12.—*Sheer elevation* and *half breadth plan* illustrating base line and showing essential reference lines, also two positions of the base line.

Thus in fig. 13, beginning at the bow end of the hull's water lines, the location of the stations are spaced off on the base line by points *a*, *b*, *c*, etc. At these points perpendiculars are erected which fix the positions of the frames or moulds.

Ques. How are the stations identified?

Ans. They are numbered 1, 2, 3, etc., as in fig. 13, beginning from the bow end.

Ques. How many stations are provided?

Ans. It depends upon the size and type of the hull.

Ques. Are the stations uniformly spaced?

Ans. Ordinarily yes, but in zones of sudden or abrupt change in body form the stations will be nearer together.

For instance, the following is an example of unequal spacing of frames or moulds being the set up for an 18-foot transom stern launch.

Table of Offsets

Mould No. 1 is 2 ft. aft of stem

" " 2 " 3 " " " section No. 1

" " 3 " 5 " " " " " 2

" " 4 " 4 " " " " " 3

" " 5 " 2 " " " " " 4

Transom " 2 " " " " " 5

L. W. L. is 1 ft. 8 in. above base.

Ques. What use besides locating frame positions is made of stations?

Ans. They are used for laying off offsets and heights.

Sheer Line.—By definition the word sheer is: *the curve given to the deck of a vessel raising it at bow and stern thus adding reserve buoyancy at either end, making the decks drier and improving the appearance of the vessel.*

Ques. How is the sheer line obtained on the drawings?

Ans. From the offset table or from height dimensions placed in the drawing at each station.

Thus in fig. 13, if distances *a*, *b*, *c*, etc., corresponding to the height (from base line) to the curved top form of the hull at stations, 1, 2, 3, etc., be laid off at those points they will be points on a curve known as the *sheer line*. The draughtsman describes this curve with aid of a spline and weights to hold the spline in position. In fig. 14, the hull is outlined by the dotted lines which show relation of sheer line.

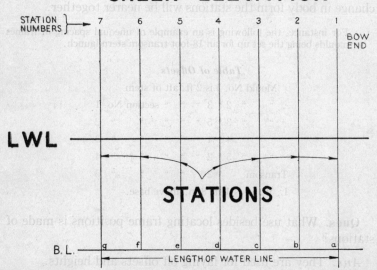

FIG. 13.—*Sheer elevation* showing *spacing of stations*.

Rabbet Line.—By definition the word *rabbet* means: 1, *to cut, as the edge of a board, in a grooved manner, so that it may form a joint with another board similarly cut;* also, to cut a rectangular groove, or recess, longitudinally in the edge of: as, a board, timber, or the like, to receive a corresponding projection upon the edge of another board, etc., so as to form a joint; 2, to lap and unite the edges of, as boards, etc., by a rabbet.

Ques. In the sheer elevation what does the rabbet line show?

Ans. It shows where the planking ends.

That is, the joint of the planking with the stem, keel and stern post.

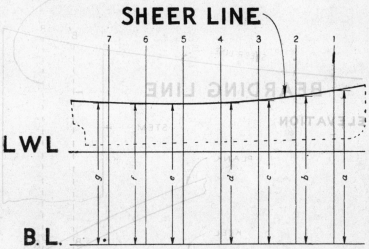

Fig. 14.—*Sheer elevation* showing method of obtaining *sheer line* by ordinate measurements referred to the base line.

Ques. How is the rabbet line determined?

Ans. Determine the angle at which sheer strake makes with the stem. Where the outside of the planking cuts the side of the stem as at R (fig. 16) is the distance of the rabbet line aft of the face of the stem.

Ques. What is the sheer strake?

Ans. The upper strake of planking on a vessel's side which follows the curve or sheer of the deck.

Bearding Line.—This is a line located where the inside of the planking crosses the half thickness of the stem as at B (fig. 16).

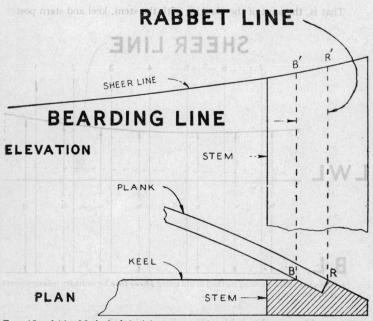

FIGS. 15 and 16.—Method of obtaining *rabbet line* and *bearding line*.

Ques. What is the space between B and R?

Ans. The rabbet or that part which must be cut out to let in the planking so that its outer surface finishes flush.

The rabbet and bearing lines for other points as a keel or stem post are determined in a similar manner.

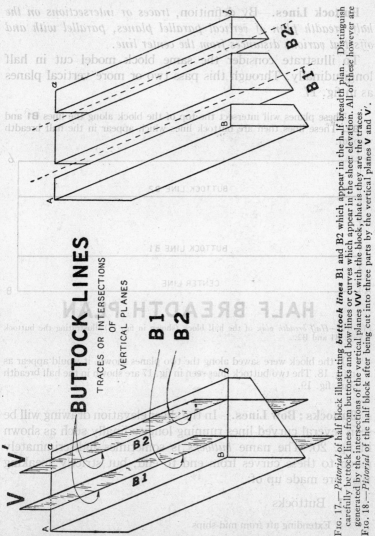

Block Lines. By definition, traces or intersections on the half breadth plan. Distinguish these however are vertical parallel planes, parallel with and of unit variation distant from the center line.

To illustrate consider the same block model cut in half longitudinally. Through this pass two or more vertical planes as in Fig. 17.

These planes will intersect the block along the lines B1 and B2. These same intersections will appear in the half breadth

HALF BREADTH PLAN

Half breadth plan of the hull block showing the intersections representing the buttock lines B1 and B2.

If the block were sawed along the two planes shown it would appear as in Fig. 18. The two buttock lines as seen in Fig. 17 are shown in the half breadth as in Fig. 19.

Buttocks; Bow Lines.—

In the sheer elevation drawing will be several curved lines running fore and aft, such as shown at ... The name buttocks is used ... approximately to these curves from ... but ... these lines ... are made up of.

Buttocks

Extending aft from mid-ships

FIG. 17.—Pictorial of half block illustrating **buttock lines** B1 and B2 which appear in the h.lf breadth plan. Distinguish carefully buttock lines from buttocks and bow lines or curves which appear in the sheer elevation. All of these however are generated by the intersections of the vertical planes VV′ with the block, that is they are the traces.

FIG. 18.—Pictorial of the half block after being cut into three parts by the vertical planes **V** and **V′**.

Buttock Lines.—By definition, *traces or intersections on the half breadth plan of vertical parallel planes, parallel with and offset at various distances from the center line.*

To illustrate consider the same block model cut in half longitudinally. Through this pass two or more vertical planes as in fig. 17.

These planes will intersect the top of the block along the lines **B1** and **B2**. These lines then are buttock lines which appear in the half breadth plan.

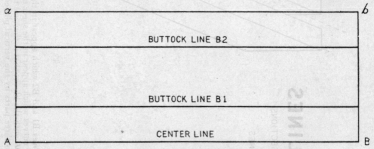

HALF BREADTH PLAN

Fig. 19.—*Half breadth plan* of the half block (shown in fig. 17) illustrating the buttock lines B1 and B2.

If the block were sawed along the two planes shown, it would appear as in fig. 18. The two buttock lines seen in fig. 17 are shown in the half breadth plan, fig. 19.

Buttocks ; Bow Lines.—In the sheer elevation drawing will be seen several curved lines running longitudinally such as shown in fig. 20. The name *buttocks* is sometimes indiscriminately given to these curves from end to end, but strictly speaking they are made up of:

1. Buttocks

Extending aft from mid-ships

2. Bow lines

Extending forward from mid-ships

This distinction is shown in the illustration (fig. 20).

These curves seen in the sheer elevation are generated by the same set of vertical parallel planes which generated the buttock lines seen in the half breadth plan (figs. 17 and 19). These planes cut the side of the hull longitudinally, the intersections generating the curves known as *buttocks* and *bow lines*.

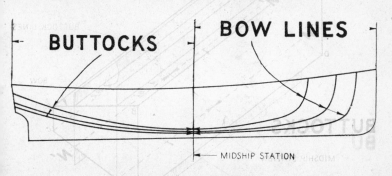

SHEER ELEVATION

Fɪɢ. 20.—*Sheer elevation* illustrating buttock and bow lines.

To illustrate, the two vertical planes **V**, **V′** seen in fig. 17 are reproduced in fig. 21 with the block turned around for better view.

Now in fig. 21, the intersections of these planes with the side of the block indicated by dotted lines **MN** and **M′N′** are the buttocks and bow lines.

Body Elevation.—This is a transverse elevation showing the contour or shape of the hull at the various stations. It is a necessary view for generating the buttocks and bow lines in the sheer elevation. In the pictorial view, fig. 21, the section B*bc*C, is a pictorial view of the body elevation which in orthographic projection is drawn as in fig. 23. Lettering is the same in both views. Now the buttocks and bow lines, shown pictorially in fig. 21, are shown orthographically in the sheer elevation, fig. 22.

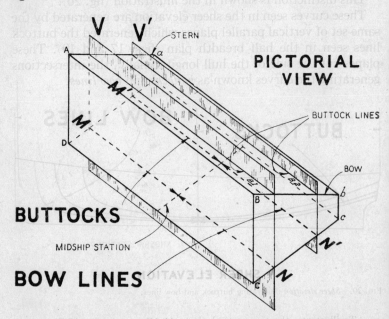

Fig. 21.—*Pictorial* of half block with the same two vertical intersecting planes **V** and **V'** illustrating *buttocks* and *bow lines* MN and M'N' in relation to the buttock lines. Note that the buttock lines are the traces B1 and B2, cut through the top and that the buttocks and bow lines are cut through the side of the block and are at different heights, shown orthographically in figs. 22 and 23.

It should be here noted that the traces N*n* and N'*n'* of the vertical parallel planes **V**, **V'** are called *verticals*. These verticals cut the side of the model at points N and N' which give the elevations of the buttocks and bow lines in the sheer elevation. Because of the shape of the block model these elevations do not vary at the different stations. However, with the usual boat models, they will differ at each station.

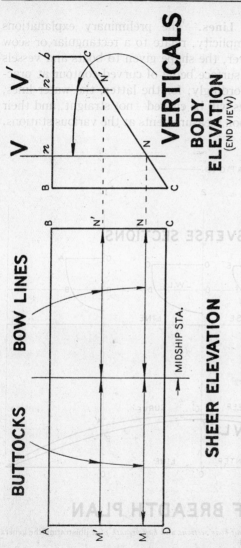

FIGS. 22 and 23.—*Sheer elevation* and *half body elevation* showing how the *buttocks* and *bow lines* are generated in the *sheer elevation* by projection from the half body elevation. It should be understood in fig. 23 that the term *"verticals,"* is an abbreviation for *vertical buttock lines,* these "verticals" being simply the end traces made by the same vertical intersecting planes that generated the (horizontal) buttock lines or just buttock lines as they are called.

To draw the buttocks and bow lines in the sheer elevation (fig. 22) project over from the body elevation the points N and N' to N and N' in fig. 22 and draw MN and M'N' giving the buttocks and bow lines at their correct elevation in the sheer elevation. Compare these straight lines with the curve obtained in fig. 27 for an actual boat.

Generating Water Lines.—The preliminary explanations thus far given, for simplicity, relate to a rectangular or scow shaped model. However, the shape given to boats and vessels is quite different, the surface being of curved contour at practically all points. Accordingly, for the latter, the water lines, buttocks and bow lines will be curved—not straight, and their generation depends upon measurements at the various stations.

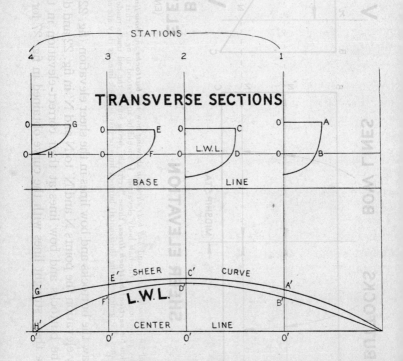

Figs. 24 and 25.—*Transverse half body sections* and *half breadth plan* illustrating the generation of (*curved*) *water lines*.

Ques. How are the water lines seen in the half breadth plan obtained?

Ans. They depend upon the offsets in the half body elevation, at the various stations.

That is, for any elevation the distance from the center of the boat to the hull surface is different at each station. These distances are called "*offsets.*"

Ques. Show how one of the water lines, say the load water line, is obtained in the half breadth plan from the half body elevation.

Ans. Fig. 24 shows transverse sections at each station and fig. 25 half breadth plan. Transfer offsets OB, OD, etc., to the half breadth plan, obtaining O'B', O'C', etc. With spline sweep a curve through points B'D'F'H' which give the load water line curve.

The sheer curve is obtained similarly.

Generating Buttocks and Bow Lines.—In the generation of these curves the hull is supposed to be cut by a series of vertical planes parallel with each other and with the longitudinal axis or center line. The traces of these cutting planes as seen in end view or half body elevation give the *verticals* which are essential in generating the buttocks and bow lines.

Ques. How are the buttocks and bow lines seen in the sheer elevation obtained?

Ans. They depend upon "heights" measured in the half body elevation at the various stations.

That is in the sheer elevation, the height of the curve at the various stations depends upon the heights measured on the vertical corresponding to the curve.

Ques. Show how one of the buttock and bow lines are obtained in the sheer elevation from the half body elevation.

Ans. Fig. 26 shows the same set of transverse sections as was shown in fig. 24 and below them the sheer elevation. Take any vertical as V, which of course is offset the same distance at each station. Transfer heights OA, OB, etc., to the sheer elevation obtaining O'A', O'B', etc. With spline sweep a curve

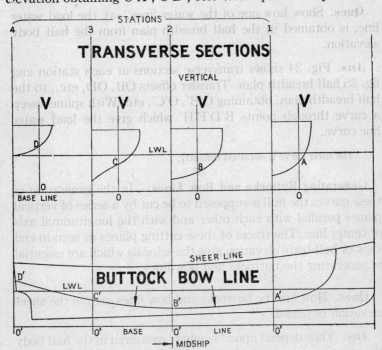

FIGS. 26 and 27.—*Transverse half body sections* and *sheer elevation* illustrating the generation of a *buttock* and *bow line*.

through points A′B′C′D′ which gives the buttock and bow line corresponding to the vertical V.

Shaping and Fairing Up.—All those who have tried to draw a "set of lines" have discovered that designing a boat is an art distinct in itself—one not acquired over night. The term "fairing up" may be defined as *the process of altering the shape of the half body sections where necessary in order that when the water lines and buttocks and bow lines are drawn in, they will be "fair" curves,* that is to say, curves without hollows or "humps."

To fair lines is an art difficult to describe because the eye is the sole judge of the fairness. It involves proper technique in the use of splines and spline weights, all of which can only be acquired by considerable practice and natural ability.

A boat built with fair curves and one with curves having dents and humps may be compared to an automobile fender before and after running into something.

To shape body sections that will give fair curves requires precision draughting and a trained eye for section shapes.

Correcting one mistake may introduce numerous other mistakes, all of which entails many alterations. In the drawing of boat lines, precision involves that:

Parallels must be exactly parallel.

Stations axes must be exactly 90° to base line.

Buttock lines must be exactly parallel with each other and with the center line.

All offsets and heights must be transferred without errors.

These requirements are essential. Errors in spacing water lines, ordinates, buttocks, etc., will make it impossible to *fair* the lines correctly.

Ques. Describe the general method of shaping the body sections.

Ans. Sketch free hand the probable shape of each section making them similar to each other, the general form being decided by type of hull and ideas of designer.

Ques. What is the next step?

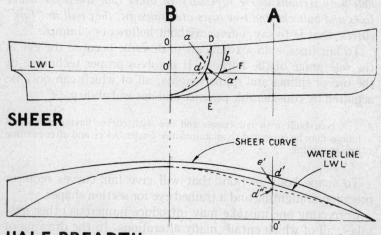

FIGS. 28 and 29.—*Sheer elevation* and *half breadth plan* illustrating **shaping the body** by *fairing up.*

Ans. The water lines and buttocks are drawn.

Ques. What is the usual procedure?

Ans. Draw in every other water line and complete the buttocks progressively.

Ques. After transferring the half breadth of a W.L. from the body sections to the half breadth plan what is the next operation?

Ans. It should be possible to sweep in a fair curve that will touch all the sections on the W.L. taken.

Ques. If the curve be not fair but irregular what should be done?

Ans. Alter the body sections to agree with the half breadth obtained in fairing a W.L. in the half breadth plan.

Sweep W.L. through the majority of the control spots and make the remaining sections agree by redrawing them.

Ques. Name one important point in drawing water lines.

Ans. The reversal of curvature.

There is a small portion of a reverse curve (where the direction of the curve reverses that is straight).

Ques. How should the straight portion be treated?

Ans. It should be lengthened somewhat in order to avoid shoulders.

Example in Shaping and Fairing Up.—In the sheer elevation and half body plan, figs. 28 and 29, an idea of the method employed is shown. In fig. 30 the half body elevation is shown considerably enlarged so that it can be plainly seen—refer to the enlarged view.

First draw **L.W.L.** and center line for the half plan view. Complete outline of hull and sweep in curve showing contour in plan at sheer strake.

Between the two fixed points (stern and transom) a midsection is sketched in to suit the eye of the designer.

In fig. 30 this is shown (enlarged) at station **B**.

Now at another station as **A**, sketch in another section as *a* (dotted). See position of station **A** in fig. 28.

Draw in the half breadth body curve *a* (dotted) by eye and sweep in water line at **L.W.L.** height.

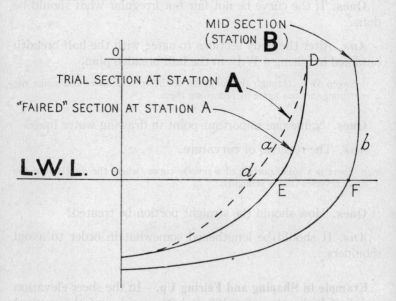

MID SECTION (STATION **B**)

TRIAL SECTION AT STATION **A**

"FAIRED" SECTION AT STATION A

L.W.L.

HALF BODY ELEVATION

Fig. 30.—*Half body elevation of fig. 28 considerably enlarged so you can see it.*

This **L.W.L.** must pass through point F of mid-section (fig. 30).

Now transfer half width of trial section on **L.W.L.** at station **A**, to the half breadth plan, fig. 29, giving the point *d* indicating by the dotted line that the shape is distorted and that section *a* must be faired up. To do this erase section *a* and lay off on **L.W.L.** the point E (fig. 30) at a distance from center line = O′e′ (fig. 28).

Sketch in new section passing through E which will pass through the water line curve at station A, indicating no distortion at that point; that is, the error has been corrected by fairing up.

However, correcting the error at this point has probably introduced many errors, with result that the fairing up process must be continued till errors in sections at every station have been properly faired. In this process they must be checked with the buttocks and bow lines as well as with the buttock lines.

Ques. What is the usual procedure?

Ans. Draw in every other water line and complete the buttocks-bow lines progressively.

By this method much erasing and altering can be avoided.

Diagonals.—By definition, diagonals are lines drawn in the half body elevation from various points on the vertical axis and at various angles.

Ques. How are diagonals located?

Ans. So that they are appxoximately normal to as many stations in the half body elevation as possible.

Ques. Why are they thus located?

Ans. Because it's easier to measure to a right angle intersection than to one at a very acute angle.

Lines of Sea Bright Sea Skiff

Sheer elevation and half breadth plan

SHEER ELEVATION

HALF BREADTH PLAN

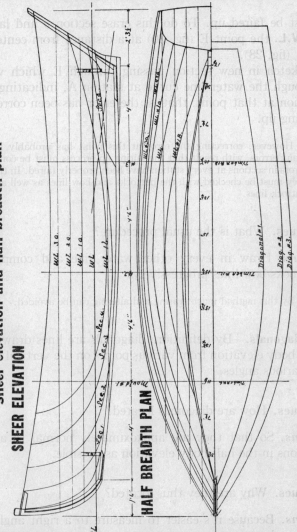

Figs. 31 to 34.—Lines for a 21′×6′6″ *Sea Bright sea skiff* designed especially for this work by the noted *Naval Architect*, *Harold Seaman* of Seaman Sea Skiffs, Inc., Long Branch, N. J. *In construction*, this skiff is lap strake or clinker built.

Lines of Sea Bright Sea Skiff—Continued

Body elevation and true contour projection of transom

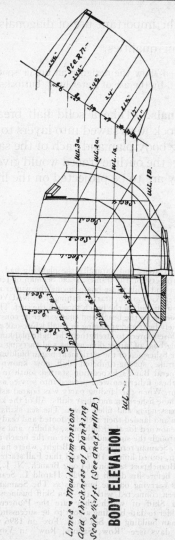

BODY ELEVATION

Lines = Mould dimensions
Add thickness of planking.
Scale ¾=ft. (See draft with B)

FIGS. 31 to 34.—*Text continued.*

In the drawings only mould sections are shown. The ortho-projected view, fig. 34, shows transom in true contour. It should be noted that the boat here shown is a *Sea Bright sea skiff* commonly called for short, just *Sea Bright skiff*.

NOTE.—Prior to 1859 the fishermen along the Jersey coast built their own skiffs from material they obtained themselves direct from the woods. All of their cedar they dressed by hand and the frames were hewn from natural crooks. These frames were hewn from natural crooks. These frames

(Continued on page 318)

Ques. What is the important use of diagonals?

Ans. Their fairing qualities.

Diagonals will often show the designer an unfair spot in the hull that could not be described by the use of water lines, buttocks and bow lines.

Projected Diagonals.—Take a solid half breadth model of hull. Now if this block were sawed into layers to correspond to the diagonals in the body plan and each of the sawn faces were laid on the drawing, the outline traced would give the shapes of the diagonal as they are to be projected on the lines.

NOTE.—*Continued from page* 317

were spaced nearly three feet apart and naturally the planking had to be lap-strake and extremely heavy to stand up between the frames. Isaac Seaman of Jersey City, N. J., followed fishing in the summer and built these boats during the winter months from 1841 to 1861. In 1859 his son, Walter A. Seaman, started fishing from NAUVOO (now Sea Bright, N. J.) where he used his skiff off and on the beach through the surf. The weight of this skiff made it very awkward to handle on the beach and that winter he constructed a skiff for his own use, planking it extremely light and springing in small white-oak ribs in one piece from gunwhale to gunwhale at close centers to strengthen the light planking. The result was an very light and easy handling boat of larger dimensions and carrying capacity than his old boat. Immediately all of the fishermen of the settlement began building new boats and thus the beginning of the lap-strake, sprung-timbered skiff now known as the Sea Bright Sea Skiff. In 1861 when General Bank's Expedition started south in the Civil War, Mr. Seaman with a number of these fishermen were pressed into service as expert surfmen and their skiffs taken with them. When the landing party was boated ashore there was not a dry gun landed except by these fishermen and their skiffs. All of the keel boats rolled down in the surf, dumped their passengers and filled down. The sea skiffs skidded out on the beach in an upright position and landed their men dry footed and ready for action. Immediately these boats became renowned for their lightness, stability and surf carrying capacity and their ability to land through the surf and skid out on the beach and set upright when aground. After the war Mr. Seaman returned to Sea Bright, where he remained until 1883. William A. Seaman, his son, joined him in 1879, and that Fall started a shop at the head of the Shrewsbury in the Branchport section of Long Branch, N. J., where he built Sea Skiffs until a few months before his death in 1929. Harold L. Seaman, his son, joined him in 1901, and today is carrying on the business as The Seaman Sea Skiff Works. The name Seaman has been connected with the Sea Skiff business for over 100 years, with the Sea Bright Sea Skiff of which they are the Pioneers for over 80 years and Seaman is the only builder to date building a boat to be successfully rowed across the Atlantic. William A. Seaman building the Sea Skiff "Fox" in 1896 which completed the voyage successfully in 54 days (see "Row, Sailors, Row" in Voyagers Unafraid, by Irving Anthony)

CHAPTER 22

Shipfitters' Blue Prints

It is impossible in a work of this size to give a lengthy treatise on blue print reading for shipfitters, but the following will give the reader a general idea of the subject.

Ques. What is the purpose of a shipfitter's blue print?

Ans. Its object is to give the loftsman the information necessary to construct the templates.

Ques. What kind of dimensions are given?

Ans. Dimensions for the finished sizes of the parts, that is, the dimensions of the work when it is completed.

The Lines.—A drawing termed the lines (explained in the preceding chapter) is worked out on a small scale.

In the case of a ship the drawing is on a smaller scale than for a boat. It is usually ¼ in. = 1 ft. The views included in the drawing are:

1. Profile or so-called sheer plan
2. Half breadth plan
3. Alleged body plan

These three views have been explained at such length in the preceding chapter that it is not necessary to treat the subject further here.

Ques. What is the most important part of loft work?

Ans. The operation of laying down on the loft floor the "lines" of the drawing full size.

Ques. What other drawings besides the "line" drawings are given to the loftsman?

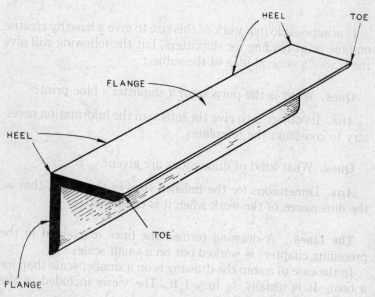

Fig. 1.—Angle bar.

Ans. A number of detail drawings.

These drawings should contain all necessary information for the mould loft for making the templates or for the iron workers to lay off material and fit it on the ship.

Ques. How many drawings would be required for say a 9000-ton ship?

Ans. Thirty drawings for the main structure and five for the superstructure.

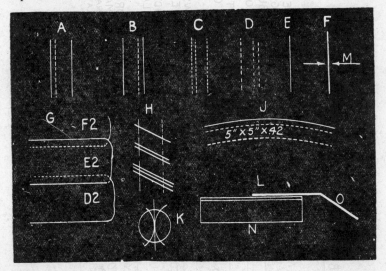

FIGS. 2 to 12.—Various conventions used on shipfitters' drawings.

Conventions.—A few of the conventions used are shown in figs. 2 to 12. In these figures:

A shows the heel of an angle bar, to be on the left, and B, the heel, to the right.

C and D, show a bar, underneath the deck, the dotted lines representing an invisible object. The heel of C, bar is left and in D, the heel is on the right.

E, a frame or transverse.

F, a heavier line than E, showing position of bulkhead; M, represents a longitudinal terminating at bulkhead, as shown by arrow points.

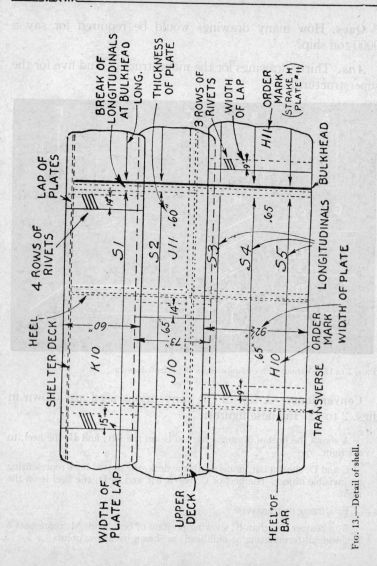

Fig. 13.—Detail of shell.

G, on shell and deck drawings, etc., arrangement of plates, showing seams. Plate E2 lies on the edges of plates D2 and F2.

The edges of the underneath plates shown by dotted lines.

H, shows lines indicating number of rows of riveting.

One line indicates single riveting. Two lines double riveting, etc.

J, showing an angle next to shell. The size, 5 inches by 5 inches by .42 of an inch, signifying an angle; if it were marked thus, 7 inches by .40 of an inch by 3½ inches by .42 of an inch, it would be a channel bar.

K, exact center of ship, as in the midship drawing.

L, shows a clip N, with a bracket riveted to the flange of clip, as shown by heavy line O.

Plates of the Hull.—The plates are in "strakes" or rows running fore and aft and beginning from the flat keel the strakes are numbered as follows:

The first strake (the garboard strake) is marked A, the next B, and so on up to the gunwale.
The letter I is not used.
The plates numbered 1, 2, 3 and so on, from the after end to the fore end. Thus, a plate marked C 6 must be three strakes up and sixth from the after end.
In fig. 12 the plates are marked H 10 and H 11, J 10 and J 11. These are called the order marks.

Ques. What does the drawing fig. 16 represent?

Ans. A section of the shell or hull.

Ques. What is given in the drawing?

Ans. The laps of the plates are shown, and dimensions are given showing the width of the laps and number of rows of rivets.

Ques What does the heavy line represent in fig. 16?

Ans. The bulkhead.

Ques. What else is shown on the drawing?

Ans. The order marks and thickness and width of plates.

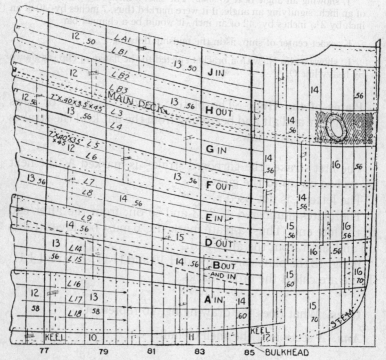

Fig. **14.**—*Fore body* detail of shell.

Ques. How are the longitudinals marked?

Ans. S1 to S5.

Note that none break through the bulkhead, shown by arrow points on both sides of the bulkhead. Heel shows position of channel or angle, the double line representing the heel. The shear mark is shown at D,

Ques. How is the number of rows of rivets indicated?

Ans. By parallel lines.

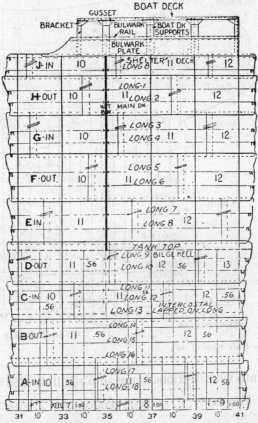

Fig. 15.—*Mid-ship* detail of shell.

Ques. Where is the width of the plates shown?

Ans. On vertical dimension lines.

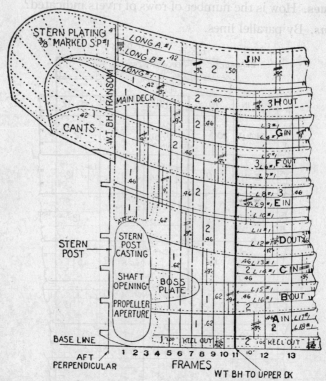

Fig. **16.**—*After body* detail of shell.

Ques. Into what sections is the ship's hull divided?

Ans. 1. Fore body; 2, midship section; and 3, after body.

These are shown in figs. 13 to 15.

Abbreviations Used on Marine Drawings.

On account of the many varying details which on the scale of the ordinary ship drawing cannot be shown plainly, ship drawings require that the various parts be accurately lettered so that there may be no doubt of the construction, dimensions or weight of material to be used.

When such lettering would be crowded on a drawing the following abbreviations may be used.

alt	Alternate
Amids	Amidships
A.P.	After perpendicular
L	Angle
L or B.A.	Bulb angle
B.R.	Boiler room
B. S.	Boiler space
Bkt.	Bracket
B.L. or	Bare line
C.B.P.	Center between perpendiculars
Cr.	Center
C or C L	Center line
⌐‾‾⌐	Channel
Coff.	Cofferdam
Coll. Blk'd	Collision bulkhead
Compt.	Compartment
C't's'k	Countersink
D or Dia	Diameter
D.R.B.L.	Double riveted butt lap

D.R.D.B.S.	Double riveted double butt strap
D.R.L.	Double riveted edge lap
D.R.S.B.S.	Double riveted single butt strap
Dbl.	Double
Dk.	Deck
E.H.	Escape hatch
E.R.	Engine room
E.S.	Engine space
F.O.	Fuel oil
F.P.	Forward perpendicular
F or Flg.	Flange
Fl.	Flange or floor (meaning will be evident)
Fr.	Frame
F.W.	Fresh water
Galv.	Galvanized
Gird.	Girder
H.R.	Half round
H.S.	Horizontal sliding
Int. or Intl.	Intercostal
½ L or ½	Half length
L & A	Light and air
L.H.	Lighting hole
Longl.	Longitudinal
L.W.L.	Load water line
Mld.	Molded
O.A.	Ordinary angle

O.T.B.	Oil tight bulkhead
O.T.F.	Oil tight floor
O.T.M.	Oil tight manhole
O.P.	Oregon pine
Pl.	Plate
Pltg.	Plating
P.O.	Petty officer
# or lbs.	Pounds
Prom.	Promenade
Q.R.B.L.	Quadruple riveted butt lap
Q.R.D.B.S.	Quadruple riveted double butt strap
Q.R.S.B.S.	Quadruple riveted single butt strap
R, r, or Rad	Radius
R.W.F.	Reserve feed water
Rev.	Reverse
S.W.B.	Salt water ballast
Sgl.	Single
S.R.B.L.	Single riveted butt lap
S.R.L.	Single riveted edge lap
□	Square
S.R.	State room
Stan	Stanchion
Stiff	Stiffener
Str	Stringer
Trans	Transverse
T.R.B.L.	Treble riveted butt lap

T.R.D.B.S.	Treble riveted double butt strap
T.R.L.	Treble riveted edge lap
T.R.S.B.S.	Treble riveted single butt strap
3/5 L	3/5 length
Vert	Vertical
W	Web
W.I.P.	Wrought iron pipe
W.P.	White pine
W.T.	Water tight
W.T.B.	Water tight bulkhead
W.T.F.	Water tight floor
W.T.M.	Water tight manhole
Y.P.	Yellow pine

CHAPTER 23

Air Craft Blue Prints

*As far as the drawings are concerned the student who has mastered the principles of **Orthographic projection** as given in this book can read any drawing. However, there are many things to be understood with respect to notation and the various data put on air craft blue prints in order to intelligently read them.*

Third angle projection is used for all drawings.

Ques. What is orthographic projection

Ans. As explained at great length in preceding chapters it is: **Parallel ray** *porjection as distinguished from* **radial** *ray projection.*

Classes of Blue Prints.—There are numerous kinds of blue prints used for study, discussion and construction of air craft. They may be classed as follows:

1. Detail prints

2. Assembly details

3. Minor assembly prints

4. Major assembly and installation prints

5. Layout prints

6. Special rework prints

Ques. What is a detail print?

Ans. A drawing of an individual part or some part of a unit which requires special information.

A detail print will give only that information required for making one part. On some drawings there is more than one detail.

Ques. What is an assembly detail print?

Ans. A drawing showing several parts with information for making and assembling them.

Ques. How is each part of an assembly detail print shown?

Ans. Each detail is completely dimensioned with all construction data needed.

Dimensions for the relative positions of all the parts are given, also data on method of assembly and holding them together.

Ques. What is a minor assembly print?

Ans. A print which differs from assembly details print in that some or all of the component parts have been fabricated from the detail prints and assembly details prints.

Ques. What should be noted about the dimensions on minor assembly prints?

Ans. They are almost all locating dimensions.

Ques. What are major assembly and installation prints?

Ans. Prints used in the construction of major assemblies such as wings, fuselage, etc.

Ques. At what stage are major assembly and installation prints used?

Ans. In final assembly only.

Ques. What is a layout print?

Ans. A drawing referred to in preparing the detail, assembly and installation drawings of the member covered by the layout. It shows complete design data.

Ques. What is a special rework print?

Ans. A drawing showing alterations to be made in an unsatisfactory part to avoid scrapping or changed to improve unsatisfactory working of a part.

Size of Drawings.—In order to facilitate folding and filing in standard letter files small drawing sheets are based on the 8½ by 11 size or an even multiple of that size.

Ques. What are the large size drawings called?

Ans. Roll size drawings.

Ques. What is the maximum roll size drawing?

Ans. 36 in. by 144 in.

The 144 in. length is the Navy limitation.

Ques. How are the commonly used drawing sizes designated?

Ans. By the letters A, B, C, D and R.

Sometimes the numerals 1, 2, 3, 4 and 5 are used in place of the letters.

The commonly used sizes are:

Size	Width	Length
A	8½	11
B	11	17
C	11	34
D	17	22
R	36 max.	144 max.

Drawing Scales.—The scales generally used for air craft drawings are:

¼   ½   full size   double   4 times size

Ques. When are drawings made to small scale?

Ans. The small scales are used for large parts of such nature that they can be clearly shown on the small scale.

Ques. What precautions should be taken where several views or sections are shown?

Ans. If they differ in scale, the scale for each should be shown in good size figures.

Ques. What is the standard notation for scales?

Ans. The scale is stated as: Quarter scale, half scale, double scale, etc.

Ques. Where is the scale shown

Ans. In the space provided for it in the "print face."

Ques. Where there are several details differing in scale from the main drawing how is this indicated?

Ans. In the title block the main scale is given and the words "*and noted*" added.

This means that different scales are used for the detail views or sections. The correct scale is placed under each detail.

Ques. What is the preferred scale for drawings?

Ans. They are made full size for parts not too large.

The choice of this scale depends upon the character of the parts. If complicated with many dimensions the full size scale will add to clearness and ease of reading the print. If the part be of simple construction a small drawing would be preferable.

Dimensions.—For air craft drawings as well as drawings in other fields, dimensioning is important.

In General:

1. Avoid where possible crossing of dimension lines.

2. Don't repeat dimensions.

3. Never omit a necessary dimension.

4. Use fine (very fine for proper contact with the lines of the object) solid dimension lines—never the dotted or dot dash variety.

5. All dimensions are expressed in inches, accordingly no inch marks are necessary and should by all means be omitted as they clutter up the drawing.

6. The air craft draughting practice that all dimensions on a drawing should be positioned to be read from

bottom of the sheet is not the best practice in the opinion of the author. (See fig. 1.).

7. A very sensible recommendation is to make decimal points heavy.

8. The recommendation that dimension limit lines should not touch the object by about $\frac{1}{16}$ inch should be disregarded unless enforced.* (See fig. 1.).

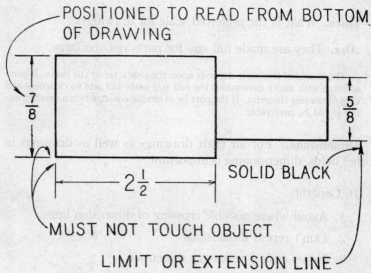

POSITIONED TO READ FROM BOTTOM OF DRAWING

$\frac{7}{8}$

$2\frac{1}{2}$

$\frac{5}{8}$

SOLID BLACK

MUST NOT TOUCH OBJECT

LIMIT OR EXTENSION LINE

Fig. 1.—Air craft draughting practice with reference to dimensioning.

9. Position dimension lines for the least interference. This is especially important where there is a multiplicity of dimensions within a small area.

---

*NOTE—If very fine lines were used for these limit lines to give positive contact between them and the lines of the object there couldn't be any possible justification in the recommendation. It certainly doesn't improve the appearance of the drawing and in the opinion of the author it looks like careless drawing.

10. For dimensioning several concentric circles use tangential limit lines rather than radii.

11. Use long or slender solid black dimension arrow heads—never the two stroke semi-visible head.

12. For a limited dimension, two numbers between the two parts of the line are used.

It means that the part will be interchangeable if the distance between the points of the arrow heads be not greater than the larger number nor less than the smaller. Limit dimensions are also given by means of the exact desired dimension followed by two other numbers one above the other. One has a plus sign before it, and when added to the exact dimension gives the largest usable dimension. By a similar process the smallest usable dimension is obtained.

Finish Notation.—This information is given on the drawing in the "title block" in the space with the listing of standard dimensional tolerances.

Ques. How many kinds of finish are indicated by placing the index number in a small circle forming the tail of the letter or finish mark?

Ans. Two.

Ques. How are these marks placed on the drawing?

Ans. Similar to the customary marks with the short and long lines intersecting on the line showing the finishing surface.

Ques. What does index number 3 indicate?

Ans. Smooth machine finish.
True machine surfaces with tool marks removed.

Ques. What does index number 5 indicate?

Ans. Rough file or grind.

Rough hand filing or rough hand grinding.

Ques. How are other machine finishes indicated?

Ans. By special notation.

Such as disc grind, etc.

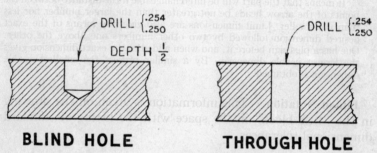

BLIND HOLE   **THROUGH HOLE**

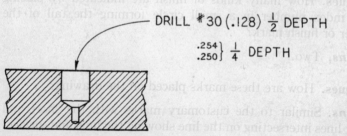

Figs. 2 to 4.—Methods of indicating drilling.

Ques. How are grinding or hardened surfaces indicated?

Ans. By placing the letter G on the line representing the surface to be ground.

For lapping use the complete word.

A few standard abbreviations which appear on Air Craft Drawings are here given:

Aileron	Ail.	Exhaust	Exh.
Altitude	Alt.	Fillet	Fil.
Approximate	Approx.	Flat head	F.H.
Army & Navy	AN.	Front	Fr.
Assembly	Assem.	Horizontal	Hor.
Attachment	Att.	Horse power	H.P.
Bill of material	B/M	Inches	In.
Bracket	Brkt.	Instrument panel	Inst. panel
Bulkhead	Blkd.	Landing gear	Ldg. gr.
Cancelled	Can.	Longeron	Long.
Cantilever	Cantil.	Longitudinal	Long.
Casting	Cstg.	Material	Matl.
Center of buoyancy	C.B.	Miles per hour	M.P.H.
Center of gravity	C.G.	Naval Aircraft Factory	N.A.F.
Center of pressure	C.P.	Reinforcement	Reinf.
Change	Chng.	Revolutions per minute	R.P.M.
Countersink	Csk.	Segment	Seg.
Design	Des.	Shock absorber	Sh. abs.
Designation	Desig.	Square inches	Sq. in.
Developed length	D.L.	Stabilizer	Stab.
Developed width	D.W.	Stiffener	Stif.
Dimension	Dim.	Superseded	Sup.
Direction finder	D/F	Trailing edge	T.E.
Elevator	Elev.	Transverse	Transv.
Engine	Eng.	Vertical	Vert.

Drilling Notation.—For most drilled holes a size tolerance is required, that is, for holes other than rivet, cotter or pilot holes. For example:

Diameter	Drill limits
$\frac{1}{8}$	$\begin{cases} .136 \\ .128 \end{cases}$
$\frac{1}{4}$	$\begin{cases} .258 \\ .250 \end{cases}$

being limits for drilled holes for rivet pins, bolts. See figs. 2 and 3.

Ques. When are pilot holes used?

Ans. When it is not practical to dimension mating holes for *match* drilling and provide the shop with a guide for drilling through the mating parts at assembly.

Ques. How are pilot drill hole sizes identified?

Ans. By normal drill size designation together with its decimal equivalent. See fig. 4.

Basic Names on Drawings.—The manufacturers of airplanes follow the U. S. Army Air Corps standard practice on all drawings.

Ques. Of what must the title of a drawing consist?

Ans. The *basic name* which comes first followed by a dash and then all description terms.

Ques. How are the description terms arranged?

Ans. In such order that it describes the piece as in ordinary language.

Ques. How is the complete title read?

Ans. Start from the dash, read all the description terms then the basic name which appears to the left of the dash, thus:

> *As written:* Rod—center section tie
>
> *As read:* Center section tie rod.

Ques. Why are titles worded as just described?

Ans. To facilitate searching through an alphabetical catalogue for a needed part, the basic name being the name looked for.

Ques. Where the basic name requires two words how is it arranged?

Ans. The naming word is put to the left of the dash and the classifying word to the right thus in the case of a two word title as *jack shaft*, for instance:

> *As written:* Shaft—landing gear jack
>
> *As read:* Landing gear jack shaft

Tabulated Drawings.—On some drawings which vary only in size, much draughting time may be saved by tabulating the varying dimensions. That is, take a drawing for a bolt for example, instead of making separate drawings for the different sizes symbols as A, B, C, D, etc., for the varying dimensions are assigned and the actual dimensions tabulated in a "block" on the drawing.

Ques. Where is the tabulation block located?

Ans. Where it can be readily seen.

Usually the tabulation block is placed at the left hand upper corner with the border lines of the drawing forming two sides of the tabulation block.

Ques. Where is it placed on roll size drawings?

Ans. To the left of and slightly above the drawing title block.

The Use of Dash Numbers.—By definition a dash number is a number having a dash prefix and following the basic drawing number, having a certain meaning and used to save time in draughting by reducing the number of drawings necessary. The various dash numbers used may be classed as:

1. To indicate left and right hand forms of a detail.

2. To indicate the sub part of an assembly which can be adequately detailed and dimensioned in its proper location on the assembly.

3. To indicate sub assemblies of a main assembly.

4. To tabulate two or more parts covered by a single drawing.

Ques. What does the basic drawing number alone indicate?

Ans. It indicates the left hand form.

Ques. How is the basic number right hand form indicated?

Ans. By the dash number "–1" joined to the basic number.

Thus A0127 indicates the left hand form.

Thus   basic   dash
                       number   number

                    A0127   –1

indicates the right hand form.

Ques. What use is made of even dash numbers as –2, –4, etc.?

Ans. They indicate left hand sub parts of an assembly.

Ques. What use is made of odd dash numbers as –3, –5, etc.?

Ans. They indicate right hand sub parts.

Ques. Mention another use of dash numbers.

Ans. They are sometimes used to identify individual pieces which may be removed as a unit from the main assembly.

Ques. Where are dash numbers located on drawings?

Ans. They should be placed within a ⅜-inch circle adjacent to the part referred to and having an arrow touching the part.

A given dash number should never be circled more than once on a given drawing.

Ques. Where are dash numbers not used?

Ans. On drawings of semi-finished castings.

The plain casting is considered as a semi-finished stage of work.

Ques. What should be noted about cancelled dash numbers?

Ans. They should never be again used.

Instead the next dash number in sequence is used.

Ques. How is the cancellation of a dash number indicated in the dash number block?

Ans. By diagonal lines (so called X) covering the cancelled space. See fig. 5.

Coded Drawings.—These are used to indicate changes. Thus frequently a detail part or minor assembly and sometimes a major assembly can be used for some other place or for some other purpose than was originally intended for it, after some minor alteration is made in the part.

Frequently only a change in one or two dimensions is all that is required, the other dimensions remaining unchanged. Such parts are made from coded drawings.

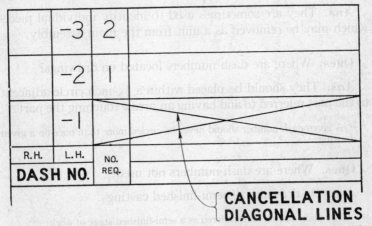

Fig. 5.—Location of dash numbers in title block and method of cancelling a dash number with so called "X" or diagonal lines. Note cancelled dash number is not removed but left in the dash number column to indicate which dash number has been cancelled.

Changes are indicated in a special code block just above the requirement block.

Ques. Describe a special code block.

Ans. It is divided into three columns as in fig. 6 for the items, part number, L and Req'd. The first column gives the same part number as that in the title block, followed by a dash number.

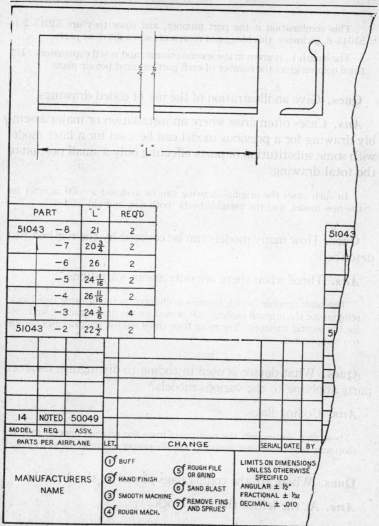

PART		"L"	REQ'D
51043	−8	21	2
	−7	20¾	2
	−6	26	2
	−5	24 1/16	2
	−4	26 11/16	2
	−3	24⅜	4
51043	−2	22½	2

14	NOTED	50049
MODEL	REQ.	ASSY.
PARTS PER AIRPLANE		

LET.	CHANGE	SERIAL	DATE	BY

MANUFACTURERS NAME	① BUFF	⑤ ROUGH FILE OR GRIND	LIMITS ON DIMENSIONS UNLESS OTHERWISE SPECIFIED
	② HAND FINISH	⑥ SAND BLAST	ANGULAR ± ½°
	③ SMOOTH MACHINE	⑦ REMOVE FINS AND SPRUES	FRACTIONAL ± 1/32
	④ ROUGH MACH.		DECIMAL ± .010

FIG. 6.—Detail of extended bulb angle wing rib stiffener with portion of title block illustrating coded drawing.

This combination is the part number, and since they are 51043–2 to 51043–8, inclusive, this blue print represents seven different parts.

The length L, is given in the second column, and is self explanatory. The third column gives the number of each part required per air plane.

Ques. Give an illustration of the use of coded drawings.

Ans. Cases often arise where an installation or major assembly drawing for a previous model can be used for a later model with some substitution of parts affecting only a small portion of the total drawing.

In such cases the original drawing can be assigned a –500 number for the new model, and the variable parts (both new and old)coded.

Ques. How many models can be covered by the method just described?

Ans. Three when there are only minor variations.

The basic number (which remains unchanged in the drawing title block) remains for the original model, –500 is used for the first variation, and –502 for the second variation. For more than three models the drawings become too complicated.

Ques. What device is used in coding to distinguish between parts applying to the various models?

Ans. Coding flags.

These flags distinguish the new parts from the original ones so that the shop may select and alter parts to form the proper assembly for each model.

Ques. Where are the coding flags placed on the drawing?

Ans. At the left of the title block.

The notation is recorded thus: for example where the installation or assembly is not l. h. or r. h.

Parts marked thus: used on 00000 (basic no.) only

Parts marked thus: used on 00000–500 only

Parts marked thus: used on 00000–502 only

All other parts used on all installations (or assemblies) called for here.

The Blue Print Face —By definition the *face* of a blue print is that space on the print enclosed by lines forming a rectangle in which are tabulated all the information data which are not directly placed on the drawing, and which are necessary for the mechanic to complete the part.

The arrangement of the face to accommodate the data placed therein depends upon the nature of the drawing and the practice of the manufacturer.

In fact it is so varied and given in so many different ways that no attempt is here made to show every arrangement.

The principal items which are arranged in sub-divisions of the face in "blocks" or columns are:

1. Title block.
2. Change block.
3. Material.
4. Scale.
5. Limits.
6. Model.
7. Dash number.
8. Part number.
9. Draughting checkers.

Among other data not given in the list are such items as: R. H., L. H., Navy, Army, finish, heat treatment, not required, etc., etc.

Ques. What is the title block?

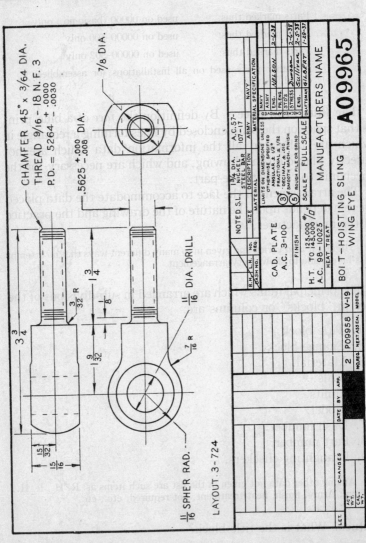

CHAMFER 45° x 3/64 DIA.
THREAD 9/16 - 18 N.F. 3
P.D. = .5264 +.0000 -.0030

7/8 DIA.

.5625 +.000 -.008 DIA.

3 3/4

3/32 R

1/4

1/8

9/32

1 3/4

11/16 DIA. DRILL

7/16 R

15/32

15/16

11/16 SPHER RAD.

LAYOUT. 3-724

NOTED S.L.

1 3/4 DIA. NICKEL STEEL BAR
SIZE DESCRIPTION
MATERIAL

CAD. PLATE
A.C. 3-100
FINISH

H.T. TO 125,000 #/□"
A.C. 98-10025
HEAT TREAT

R.H. L.H. NO. DASH NO. REQ

LIMITS ON DIMENSIONS UNLESS OTHERWISE SPECIFIED
ANGULAR ± 1/2°
FRACTIONAL ± 1/32
③ DECIMAL ± .010
SMOOTH MACH. FINISH
⑤ ROUGH FILE OR GRIND

MATERIAL SPECIFICATION
A.C. 57-107-17
DESCRIPTION

NAVY ARMY NAVY
APPROVED
ARMY   NELSON   2-6-37
R.ENG
PR.ENG
STO'S
STRESS   Duncan   2-6-37
CHECKED   Sullivan   2-5-37
ENG.   Sullivan   1-29-37
DRAFTSMAN   GILBERT

SCALE— FULL SCALE

MANUFACTURERS NAME

BOLT-HOISTING SLING
WING EYE

A09965

2   P09958   V-19
NO.REQ   NEXT ASSEM.   MODEL

LET.   CHANGES   DATE BY APP.

ACT. WT.
CAL. WT.

Fig. 7.—Drawing of a machine part showing title block notations.

Ans. That space provided for the name of the manufacturer, the name and number of the part or parts shown in the drawing.

The names of the engineers responsible for the drawings given in their own handwriting. Other items are model and serial number of the plane, also date.

Ques. What is the bill of material?

Ans. A listing of all the separate parts and number of each required to complete the part shown on the print.

Ques. What is the change block?

Ans. The space provided for listing any changes, that is, alterations of the original drawing.

Ques. What else is included in the change block?

Ans. Names of draughtsmen and engineers responsible for the change and serial number of first plane built with the changes.

Ques. How is each change identified on the drawing?

Ans. By means of a letter placed on drawing, at the front where the change is to be made or as near thereto as possible.

Ques. How are several changes listed?

Ans. The same letter is used for each change with an identifying numeral subscript.

Reading Air Craft Prints.—As before stated so far as the drawings are concerned any one who has mastered the principles of orthographic projection as given in this book can read

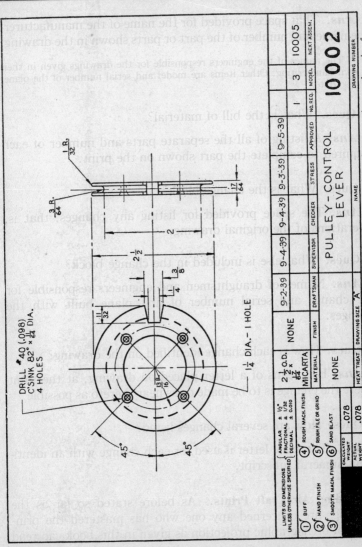

Fig. 8.—Side and end views of pulley control lever illustrating detail prints and reading of the notation on the print face.

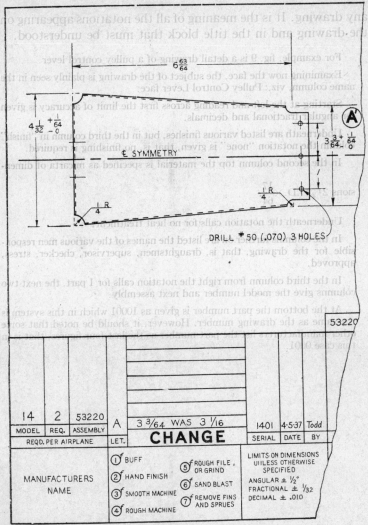

Fig. 9.—Plan of rib-empennage-elevator illustrating change block.

any drawing. It is the meaning of all the notations appearing on the drawing and in the title block that must be understood.

For example, fig. 9 is a detail drawing of a pulley control lever.

Examining now the face, the subject of the drawing is plainly seen in the name column, viz.: Pulley Control Lever face.

Starting at the left and reading across first the limit of accuracy is given for angular fractional and decimals.

Underneath are listed various finishes, but in the third column in "finish" column the notation "none" is given, that is, no finishing is required.

In the second column top the material is specified as micarta of dimensions $2\frac{1}{2}$ O.D. $\times \frac{17}{64}$.

Underneath the notation calls for no heat treatment.

In the columns further on are listed the names of the various men responsible for the drawing, that is, draughtsmen, supervisor, checker, stress, approved.

In the third column from right the notation calls for 1 part, the next two columns give the model number and next assembly.

At the bottom the part number is given as 10001 which in this system is the same as the drawing number. However, it should be noted that some other manufacturers list the part number as the last four figures, that is in this case 0001.

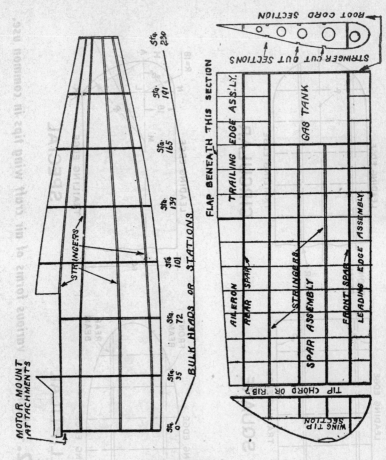

PLATE 1.

Sectional views of fuselage and wing framework of typical air craft.

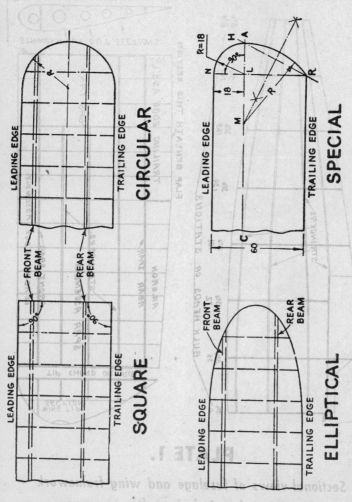

PLATE 2. — *Illustrating various forms of air craft wing tips in common use.*

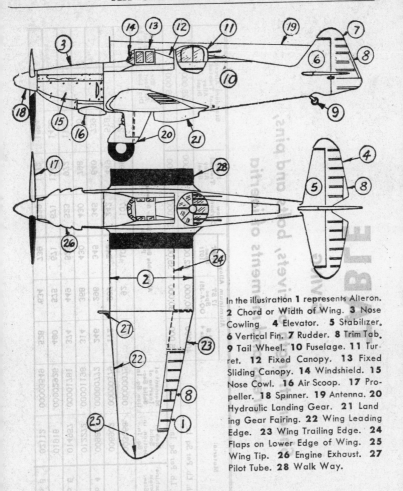

In the illustration **1** represents Aileron. **2** Chord or Width of Wing. **3** Nose Cowling. **4** Elevator. **5** Stabilizer. **6** Vertical Fin. **7** Rudder. **8** Trim Tab. **9** Tail Wheel. **10** Fuselage. **11** Turret. **12** Fixed Canopy. **13** Fixed Sliding Canopy. **14** Windshield. **15** Nose Cowl. **16** Air Scoop. **17** Propeller. **18** Spinner. **19** Antenna. **20** Hydraulic Landing Gear. **21** Landing Gear Fairing. **22** Wing Leading Edge. **23** Wing Trailing Edge. **24** Flaps on Lower Edge of Wing. **25** Wing Tip. **26** Engine Exhaust. **27** Pilot Tube. **28** Walk Way.

PLATE 3.

Schematic drawings of an English pursuit Bomber.

TABLE

GIVING

Shear strength of rivets, bolts and pins, areas and moments of inertia

Material		Aluminum Alloy			Low Carbon Steel	Heat Treated Alloy Steel	Standard Aircraft, Heat Treated Alloy Steel	
		A-17 S Grade 4	17 ST Spec OO-A-351	24 ST Spec 11071				
Tensile Strength, Lb. Per Sq. In.		40,000	50,000	62,000	55,000	100,000	125,000	
Shear Strength, Lb. Per Sq. In.		25,000	30,000	35,000	35,000	65,000	75,000	

Size of Rivet, Pin or Bolt	Machine Screw Size	Area of Solid Section in Sq. In.	Moment of Inertia of Solid Section Sq. In.	Allowable Single Shear Strength Pounds						Ten. Str. At Root Dia. Lbs.	Yield Str. at Root D. Lb.
1/16		.003068	.00000075	77	92	107	107	199	230		
3/32		.006902	.00000379	172	207	242	242	449	518		
.112	No. 4	.009852	.00000772	246	296	345	345	640	739		
1/8		.012272	.00001198	314	368	430	430	798	920		
.138	No. 6	.014957	.00001781	374	449	523	523	972	1122		
5/32		.01918	.00002926	480	575	671	671	1247	1438		
.164	No. 8	.02112	.00003549	528	634	739	739	1372	1584		

TABLE

GIVING

Properties of rivets, bolts and pins — Continued

Size	Area	I								
3/16	.02761	.00006066	690	828	966	966	1794	2070	2136	1709
.190 (No. 10)	.02835	.00006399	709	850	992	992	1842	2126		
.216 (No. 12)	.03664	.0001069	916	1099	1282	1282	2381	2748		
7/32	.03758	.0001125	940	1127	1315	1315	2442	2818		
1/4	.04908	.0001918	1227	1472	1717	1717	3190	3681	3982	3186
5/16	.07669	.0004682	1917	2300	2684	2684	4984	5751	6429	5143
3/8	.1105	.0009710	2762	3315	3868	3868	7183	8287	9953	7962
7/16	.1503	.001797	3757	4509	5261	5261	9770	11272	13433	10746
1/2	.1963	.003069	4907	5889	6871	6871	12760	14722	18356	14685
9/16	.2485	.004914	6212	7455	8697	8697	16152	18637	23313	18650
5/8	.3068	.007492	7670	9204	10738	10738	19942	23010	29676	23741
3/4	.4418	.01553	11045	13254	15463	15463	28717	33135	43494	34795
7/8	.6013	.02878	15032	18039	21046	21046	39085	45097	59515	47612
1	.7854	.04908	19635	23562	27489	27489	51051	58905	80159	64127

For double shear multiply by 2

AIR CRAFT
Blue Print Symbols

When working with a blueprint, one will find that the rivets, bolts, etc., are represented as numbers—AN 430 D 4—4. AN signifies that the part is under Army and Navy specifications. 430 shows that the part is a round head rivet. D stands for dural.

The first 4 gives the diameter of the rivet in 32nds. $\frac{4}{32}$ equals $\frac{1}{8}$. The second 4 gives the length of the rivet in 16ths. $\frac{4}{16}$ equals $\frac{1}{4}$. If the D is not present, it represents steel parts.

The following are different **types of rivets under AN code.**

AN 420 Countersunk   AN 425 Countersunk   AN 430 Round Head
AN 441 Flat Head   AN 442 Flat Head   AN 455 Brazier Head

Diameters and lengths can be determined as shown.
Obtain the type of rivets specified on the print from the icebox.
Don't take more than enough rivets to last for one-half an hour. Rivets become hard after that period.
Some of the other parts such as screws, nuts, bolts, etc., that come under Army and Navy specifications are listed below.

AN 3 Bolt—Hex. Head #10–32	AN 4 Bolt—Hex. Head $\frac{1}{4}$–20
AN 5 " " " #$\frac{5}{16}$–28	AN 6 " " " $\frac{3}{8}$–24
AN 7 " " " #$\frac{7}{16}$–20	AN 8 " " " $\frac{1}{2}$–20
AN 9 " " " #$\frac{9}{16}$–18	AN 10 " " " $\frac{5}{8}$–18
AN 12 " " " #$\frac{3}{4}$–16	AN 14 " " " $\frac{7}{8}$–14
AN 16 " " " #1 –14	AN 21 Bolt Clevis # 6–40

AN 22 Bolt Clevis	#8 –36	AN 23 " "	#10–32
AN 24 " "	#1/4–28	AN 25 " "	#5/16–24
AN 26 " "	#3/8–24	AN 27 " "	#7/16–20
AN 28 " "	#1/2–20	AN 29 " "	#9/16–18
AN 30 " "	#5/8–18	AN 32 " "	#3/4–16
AN 34 " "	#7/8–14	AN 36 " "	# 1–14
AN 42 Eye Bolt	3/16P#10–32	AN 43 Eye Bolt	#1/4–28
AN 44 " "	1/4P#5/16–24	AN 45 " "	5/16P#5/16–24
AN 46 " "	3/8P#3/8–24	AN 47 " "	3/8P#7/16–20
AN 48 " "	7/16P#1/2–20	AN 49 " "	1/2P#9/16–18

AN 73 Hex. Bolt Aircraft Drilled head 10A preceding dash number shows

AN 74	"	"	"	"		1/4
AN 75	"	"	"	"		5/16
AN 76	"	"	"	"		3/8
AN 77	"	"	"	"		7/16
AN 78	"	"	"	"		1/2
AN 80	"	"	"	"		5/8
AN 81	"	"	"	"		3/4

coarse thread and no letter
fine thread.
73–81 drilled head
AN 73 A 10
AN 73 10

AN 100 Thimble Wire Cable		AN 111 Bushing Cable
AN 115 Shackle Cable		AN 130 Turnbuckle Ass. Eye. and Fork
AN 135 Turnbuckle Ass. Eye and Pin Eye		
AN 140 Turnbuckle Ass. Cable Eye		AN 155 Turnbuckle Barrel
AN 160 Turnbuckle Fork		AN 165 " Eye—for pin
AN 170 " Eye for Cable		AN 200 Bearing—Heavy Duty
AN 201 Bearing—Intermediate		AN 210 Pulley Control
AN 226 Fastener—Cowl Post Type		AN 230 Grommet
AN 235 Hook Lacing		AN 240 Eyelet Lacing
AN 250 Hinge—Butt		AN 251 Hinge—Continuous
AN 275 Joint—Ball and Socket		AN 286 Fitting—Lubrication
AN 287 Fitting—Lubrication		AN 295 Cup—Oil
AN 310 Nut—Castellated		AN 315 Nut—Plain Hexagon
AN 316 NUT—Check—Hex.		AN 320 Nut—Shear
AN 340 Nut—Hex. Coarse		AN 345 Nut—Hex.—Fine
AN 350 Nut—Wing		AN 355 Nut—Slotted—Hex.
AN 360 Nut—Engine Plain		AN 365 Nut—Stop
AN 366 Nut—Anchor		AN 367 Nut—Anchor
AN 380 Pin—Cotter (Steel)		Plain Dash Carbon. C cor. resist.
AN 392 Pin Flat Head 1/8		

AN 394 " " "	1/4	AN 393 Pin Flat Head 3/16	
AN 396 " " "	3/8	AN 395 " " "	5/16
AN 398 " " "	1/2	AN 397 " " "	7/16
AN 400 " " "	5/8	AN 399 " " "	9/16
AN 404 " " "	7/8	AN 402 " " "	3/4
AN 415 Pin—Lock		AN 406 " " "	1
AN 425 Rivet 78° Countersunk		AN 420 Rivet 90° Countersunk	
AN 435 Rivet Rd Hd Iron, Copper		AN 430 Rivet Round Head	

AN 441	Rivet Flat Head Iron and Copper			
AN 442	Rivet Flat Head	AN 450	Rivet Tub. Oval Head	
AN 445	Rivet Brazier Head	AN 481	Terminal Eng. Control	
AN 486	Terminal Eng. Control	AN 490	Rod End	
AN 502	Mach. Screw—Fillister	AN 505	Mach. Screw Flat Head	
AN 510	" " Flat Head	AN 515	" " Round Head	
AN 520	" " Round "	AN 526	" " Button Head	
AN 535	Screw—Drive	AN 661	Terminal—Spark Plug	
AN 665	Tie Rod Terminal	AN 671	Tie Rod Streamline	
AN 673	Tie Rod Streamline 10–32	AN 674	" " "	¼–28
AN 675	" " " 5⁄16–24	AN 676	" " "	⅜–24
AN 677	" " " 7⁄16–20	AN 678	" " "	½–20
AN 679	" " " 9⁄16–18	AN 680	" " "	⅝–18
AN 682	" " " ¾–16	AN 684	" " "	⅞–14
AN 686	" " " 1–14	AN 701	Tie Rod Internal	6–40
AN 703	Tie Rod Internal 10–32	AN 704	" " "	¼–28
AN 705	" " " 5⁄16–24	AN 706	" " "	⅜–24
AN 707	" " " 7⁄16–20	AN 708	" " "	½–20
AN 740	Clamp—Tube	AN 741	Clamp	
AN 746	Clamp—Hose	AN 771	Cock—Drain	
AN 775	Bolt—Universal Fit.	AN 776	Elbow 90°	
AN 777	Elbow 75°	AN 778	Elbow 45°	
AN 780	Nipple Union	AN 785	Coupling Union	
AN 790	Elbow Union	AN 795	Tee Union	
AN 800	Cone Union	AN 805	Nut Union	
AN 815	Union—flared tube	AN 816	Connector—Fl. Tube	
AN 817	Nut—Sleeve Coupling	AN 818	Nut Coupling	
AN 819	Sleeve Coupling	AN 820	Cap—Flared Tube	
AN 821	Elbow—Fared Tube 90	AN 822	Elbow Tube—Thread	
AN 823	" " "– Thread	AN 824	Tee—Flared Tube	
AN 825	Tee Tube and Thread	AN 826	Tee Tube—Thread	
AN 827	Cross Tube	AN 828	Union—Tube	
AN 830	Tee—Tube	AN 831	Nut—Tube	
AN 840	Nipple—Thread	AN 842	Elbow—Thread 90°	
AN 843	Elbow—Tube 90°	AN 845	" " 45°	
AN 910	Coupling Thread	AN 911	Nipple Thread	
AN 912	Bushing Reducer	AN 913	Plug—Thread	
AN 914	Elbow—Thread 90°	AN 915	Elbow—Thread 45°	
AN 916	" " 90°	AN 917	Tee—Thread	
AN 918	Cross—Thread	AN 931	Grommet Round	
AN 935	Lock Washer	AN 960	Washer—Plain	
AN 970	Washer—Flat Wood	AN 996	Ring—Lock Engine	

The specifications are without any letter after the identifying figures and as such represent steel. If D is added (AN 3 D6), it will signify that the part is made of dural

AN 3—6. A bolt, standard hexagon head, and made of steel. The first number gives the diameter in 16ths and the last number gives the lengths in 8ths.

AN 310—3. A standard hexagon castellated nut made of steel The dash number specifies the diameter of the bolt in 16ths which will fit the nut.

AN 320. A shear nut made of steel with a hexagon head. It has less height than AN 310. Used with clevis bolt where tension is small.

AN 960. A plain washer. The diameter of the screw is added and its thickness to show the worker what type washer to use. AN 960 D 10— 064. Plain washer to fit a #10 screw. The washer is .064 thick. Made of dural.

AN 520 D 10—8. A round head screw made of dural. The 10 stands for the size of the screw. (10-32.) The 8 stands for the length in 16ths of an inch. 8/16 equals ½.

AN 380 I—2. A low carbon steel cotter pin. The first number specifies the diameter of the cotter pin in 32nds while the second specifies the length of the cotter pin in ¼ths.

The blackened section in the illustrations figs 22 and 24 of the stop nut and anchor nut represents fiber The fiber diameter is smaller than the diameter of the screw When the screw is tightened in the nut, it must tap threads in the fiber The fiber holds the screw in place and will not allow it to become loose, due to the vibration set up in flight.

Screw threads should always extend from 2 to 2½ threads beyond the nut. If the screw does not, replace with one that will.

If it does not extend the desired amount, the desired strength will be lost. If it extends too far, cut off the screw until the proper length is reached. File cut edge smooth.

Note the illustration fig. 15 showing proper method of fastening cotter pins. Use threadlube on the screw when it is to be used with stop or anchor nut.

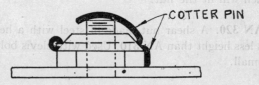

Fig. 15.—Showing proper method of bending **cotter pin** in aircraft assembly.

Anchor nuts are used where it would be difficult to reach with a wrench. The nut is riveted to the part. The rivet on the surface of the part is usually flush to allow assembling other sections such as hand hole covers, etc.

Nuts and bolts should be primed before being assembled. Also touch up the heads after tightening.

As there are many vital parts to an airplane that require adjusting, it is necessary to leave openings in the skin to reach them.

A Dzus fastener is used to hold the covers in place in flight.

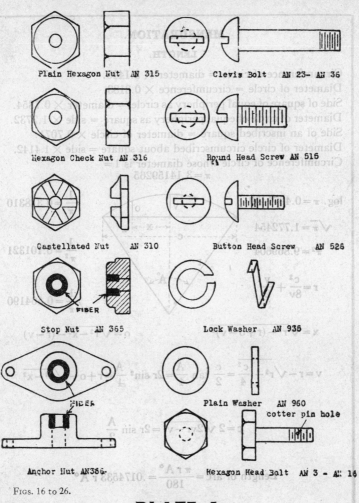

Plain Hexagon Nut AN 315   Clevis Bolt AN 23- AN 36

Hexagon Check Nut AN 316   Round Head Screw AN 515

Castellated Nut AN 310   Button Head Screw AN 526

Stop Nut AN 365   Lock Washer AN 935

Plain Washer AN 960
cotter pin hole

Anchor Nut AN366   Hexagon Head Bolt AN 3 - AN 16

FIGS. 16 to 26.

PLATE 4.

Various forms of nuts and bolts used in air craft assembly.

MENSURATION.

LENGTH.

Circumference of circle = diameter × 3.1416.
Diameter of circle = circumference × 0.3183.
Side of square of equal periphery as circle = diameter × 0.7854.
Diameter of circle of equal periphery as square = side × 1.2732.
Side of an inscribed square = diameter of circle × 0.7071.
Diameter of circle circumscribed about square = side × 1.4142.
Circumference of circle whose diameter is 1 =
$$\pi = 3.14159265$$

$\log. \pi = 0.4971499$

$\sqrt{\pi} = 1.772454$

$\pi^2 = 9.869604$

$r = \dfrac{c^2}{8v} + \dfrac{v}{2}$

$\dfrac{1}{\pi} = 0.318310$

$\dfrac{1}{\pi^2} = 0.101321$

$\sqrt{\dfrac{1}{\pi}} = 0.564190$

$x = \sqrt{r^2 - (r + o - v)^2}$

$o = \sqrt{r^2 - x^2} - (r - v)$

$v = r - \sqrt{r^2 - \dfrac{c^2}{4}} = \dfrac{c}{2}\tan\dfrac{A}{4} = 2r\sin^2\dfrac{A}{4} = r + o - \sqrt{r^2 - x^2}$

$c = 2\sqrt{2vr - v^2} = 2r\sin\dfrac{A}{2}$

Length of arc $= \dfrac{\pi r A^\circ}{180} = .0174533\, r\, A^\circ$

Angle $A^\circ = \dfrac{180 \times arc}{\pi r} = \dfrac{57.29578 \times arc}{r}$

SURFACES AND VOLUMES OF SOLIDS.

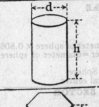

CYLINDER

Convex Surface $= \pi dh$

Total Surface $= \pi dh + \dfrac{\pi d^2}{2}$

Volume $= \dfrac{\pi}{4} d^2 h$

Volume Cylinder, right or oblique $=$ area of section at right angles to sides $\times$ length of side.

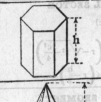

PRISM

Lateral Surface $= h \times$ Base Perimeter
Total Surface $=$ Lateral Surface $+ (2 \times$ Base Area$)$
Volume $= h \times$ Base Area

PYRAMID

Lateral Surface $= \dfrac{s}{2} \times$ Base Perimeter

Total Surface $=$ Lateral Surface $+$ Base Area

Volume $= \dfrac{h}{3} \times$ Base Area

Center of Gravity $= \dfrac{h}{4}$, above base

FRUSTUM OF PYRAMID

Lateral Surface $= s($Top $+$ Base Perimeters$) \div 2$
If $a =$ top area and $A =$ base area,
Total Surface $=$ Lateral Surface $+ (a + A)$
Volume $= h(a + A + \sqrt{aA}) \div 3$
Center of Gravity $= \dfrac{h}{4}\left(\dfrac{3a + A + 2\sqrt{aA}}{a + A + \sqrt{aA}}\right)$
above base

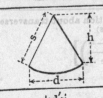

CONE

Convex Surface $= \dfrac{\pi}{2} ds = \dfrac{\pi d}{4}\sqrt{d^2 + 4h^2}$

Total Surface $=$ Convex Surface $+ \dfrac{\pi d^2}{4}$

Volume $= \dfrac{\pi}{12} d^2 h = \dfrac{\pi}{24} d^3 \sqrt{4s^2 - d^2}$

Center of Gravity above base $= \dfrac{h}{4}$

FRUSTUM OF CONE

Convex Surface $= \dfrac{\pi s}{2}(d + d') = \dfrac{\pi}{4}(d + d')\sqrt{4h^2 + (d - d')^2}$

Total Surface $= \dfrac{\pi s}{2}(d + d') + \dfrac{\pi}{4}(d^2 + d'^2)$

Volume $= \dfrac{\pi h}{12}(d^2 + dd' + d'^2)$

Center of Gravity above base $= \dfrac{h(d^2 + 2dd' + 3d'^2)}{4(d^2 + dd' + d'^2)}$

SURFACES AND VOLUMES OF SOLIDS.

SPHERE

Surface $= \pi d^2 = 4\pi r^2$

Volume $= \dfrac{\pi d^3}{6} = \dfrac{4}{3}\pi r^3$

Side of an equal cube $=$ diameter of sphere $\times 0.806$

Length of an equal cylinder $=$ diameter of sphere $\times 0.6667$

Center of Gravity of Half Sphere $= \frac{3}{8}r$ above spherical center

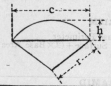

SPHERICAL SECTOR

Total Surface $= \dfrac{\pi r}{2}(4h + c)$

Volume $= \frac{2}{3}\pi r^2 h = \frac{2}{3}\pi r^2 \left(r - \sqrt{r^2 - \dfrac{c^2}{4}} \right)$

Center of Gravity above center of sphere $= \frac{3}{4}\left(r - \dfrac{h}{2} \right)$

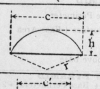

SPHERICAL SEGMENT

Spherical Surface $= 2\pi rh = \pi(c^2 + 4h^2) \div 4$

Total Surface $=$ Spherical Surface $+ (\pi c^2 \div 4)$

Volume $= \pi h^2(3r - h) \div 3 = \pi h(3c^2 + 4h^2) \div 24$

Center of gravity above base of segment $= h(4r - h) \div 4(3r - h)$

SPHERICAL ZONE

Convex Surface $= 2\pi rh$

Total Surface $= 2\pi rh + \dfrac{\pi}{4}(c^2 + c'^2)$

Volume $= \dfrac{\pi h}{24}(3c^2 + 3c'^2 + 4h^2)$

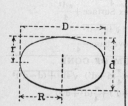

ELLIPSOID (I. Revolution about transverse axis)

Surface $= 2\pi r\left[r + R\left(\dfrac{\sin^{-1} e}{e} \right) \right]$

Volume $= \dfrac{4}{3}\pi Rr^2$

ELLIPSOID (II. Revolution about conjugate axis)

Surface $= \pi\left[2R^2 + \dfrac{2.302r^2}{e}\log.\left(\dfrac{1+e}{1-e} \right) \right]$

Volume $= \dfrac{4}{3}\pi R^2 r$ Where $e = \dfrac{\sqrt{R^2 - r^2}}{R}$

CHAPTER 24

The Slide Rule

The principle of the slide rule is based on the fact that *the addition of logarithms multiplies the numbers that they represent and the subtraction of logarithms divides the numbers.*

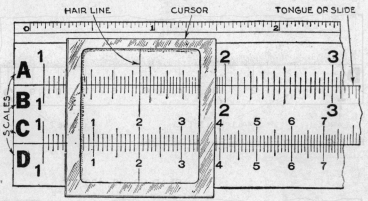

FIG. 1.—Detail of slide rule showing scales and parts. Note especially the scales as they are constantly referred to by letter, as scale **C**, scale **D**, etc.

By use of the slide rule the operations of multiplication, division, the finding of powers and the extraction of roots, may be performed rapidly and with an approximation to accuracy which is sufficient for many purposes.

With a good 10 inch rule the results obtained are usually accurate to ¼ of 1 per cent.

A slide rule has four scales as shown in fig. 1 and designated by the letters A,B,C,D. The two outer scales A and D, are stationary, but the two inner scales B and C, are on a tongue arranged to slide between the two outer scales.

The chief difficulty in learning to use the slide rule is to learn to read the graduations on the scales.

Taking first part of the D scale and beginning at the left hand end it will be seen in fig. 2, that between the large 1 and 2 there are ten divisions indicated by the small figures 1, 2, 3, etc.

Now, in fig. 3 the large 1 is read 1 and since there are 10 large divisions between large 1 and large 2, the reading at small 2 for instance is 1.2, 12,

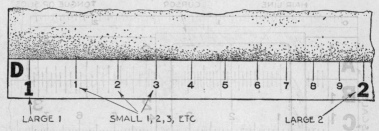

FIG. 2.—Detail of **D** scale showing large and small figures.

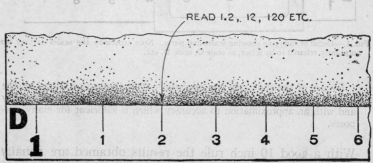

FIG. 3.—Detail of **D** scale showing how to read 1.2, 12, 120, etc.

120, etc. Hence it will be noted that the slide rule does not place the decimal point.

It will be further noted that between each of the divisions designated by small 1, 2, etc., there are 10 smaller divisions (fig. 1). Hence each one of these is one hundredth of the large division from large 1 to large 2. This permits reading accurately a number of three figures and by "guess" a number of four figures. Thus to read 1 1 3, read the big 1 (for 100), then the small 1 (for 10) and finally the third hundredths division (for 3) counting to the right from the little 1 division as indicated in fig. 4.

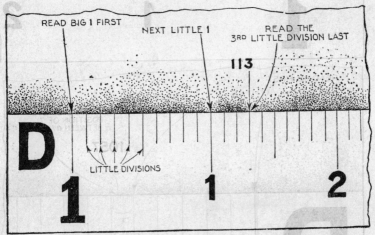

FIG. 4.—Detail of **C** scale showing how to read numbers such as 113.

To read a number such as 104, remember that the big 1 can be read either 1 or 10. Hence call the big 1 ten and count 4 of the little divisions to the right as in fig. 5.

The accuracy with which a number of four figures can be read depends upon the ability of the eye to gauge the position of the 4th figure between two of the small divisions. Thus, in fig. 6, to read the number 1,057 take big 1 for the first two figures, that is 10; count to right from big 1 five of the little divisions indicated by *a*, for the third figure.

Now the fourth figure is found between the two adjacent little divisions *a* and *b*. The illustration which is greatly magnified shows *a,b*, divided

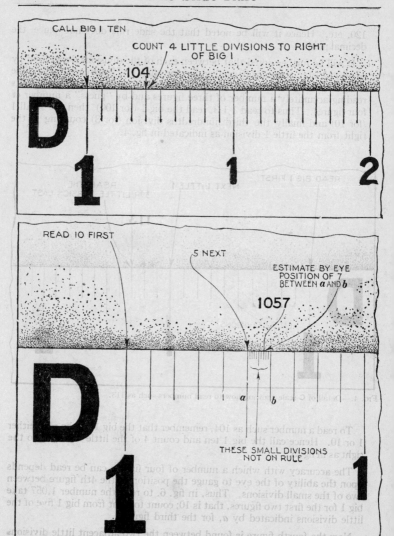

To read a number such as 104, remember that the big 1 is no longer 1 or 10. Hence call the big 1 ten and count 4 of the little divisions to the right as indicated in fig. 5.

The accuracy with which a number of four figures can be read depends upon the ability of the eye to gauge the position of the 4th figure between two of the small divisions. Thus, in fig. 6, to read the number 1,057, take big 1 for the first two figures, that is 10; count to the right from big 1 five of the little divisions indicated by a, for the third figure.

Now the fourth figure is found between the two adjacent little divisions a and b. The illustration, which is greatly magnified, shows a, b, divided into 10 divisions, but these divisions are not on the rule itself and must be judged or guessed at "by the eye" and upon the precision with which this is done depends the accuracy of the fourth figure or in this case the 7 of the number 1057.

To read numbers beginning with 2, 3, etc., start with the big 2, big 3, etc., and proceed similarly as in the foregoing explanations.

Thus to read the number 275, read first in fig. 7, the big 2; count off seven small divisions to right, that is to division *a*, and then gauge by eye half the distance or 5 invisible divisions between *a* and *b* obtaining the number 275.

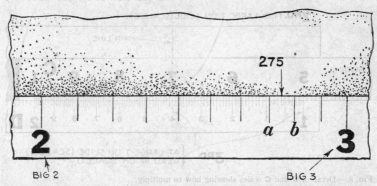

Fig. 7.—Detail of **D** scale showing how to read numbers of three figures beginning with 2, 3, etc.

Example.—Multiply 2×7.

In fig. 8 slide last division or "index" at right end of C scale opposite big 2 on D scale. Move "cursor" (the sliding glass with hair line) opposite big 7 on C scale and read 14 on D scale indicated by the hair line.

The "index" at either end may be used, but if the second factor come "off the scale" take the index at the other end of the tongue.

Refer to illustrations on page 4.

Fig. 5.—Detail of **D** scale showing how to read numbers containing a cipher (or ciphers) such as 104.

Fig. 6.—Detail of **D** scale showing how to read a number of four figures.

Example.—Divide 4 by 2.

In fig. 9 slide cursor till hair line registers with large 4 on **D** scale; slide tongue to register large 2 (on **C** scale) with hair line. At large 1 on the end of tongue (scale **C**) read 2 on scale **D,** which is the answer.

Example.—Divide 475 by 23.

In fig. 10 slide cursor till hair line registers with 475 on scale **D**; slide tongue until 23 on scale **C,** registers with 475 on scale **D.** At large 1 on end

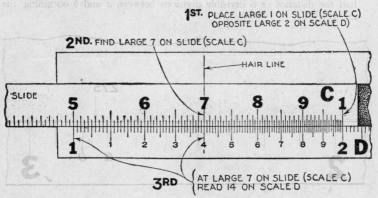

1ST. PLACE LARGE 1 ON SLIDE (SCALE C) OPPOSITE LARGE 2 ON SCALE D

2ND. FIND LARGE 7 ON SLIDE (SCALE C)

HAIR LINE

SLIDE

3RD AT LARGE 7 ON SLIDE (SCALE C) READ 14 ON SCALE D

FIG. 8.—Detail of **D** and **C** scales showing how to multiply.

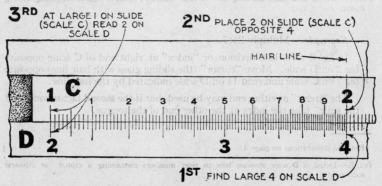

3RD AT LARGE 1 ON SLIDE (SCALE C) READ 2 ON SCALE D

2ND PLACE 2 ON SLIDE (SCALE C) OPPOSITE 4

HAIR LINE

1ST FIND LARGE 4 ON SCALE D

FIG. 9.—Detail of **D** and **C** scales showing how to divide numbers of one figure each.

of tongue read 2,065 (scale **D**) and place the decimal point to read 20.65. As the slide rule does not give the decimal point this has to be done

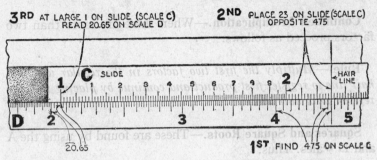

3RD AT LARGE 1 ON SLIDE (SCALE **C**) READ 20.65 ON SCALE **D**

2ND PLACE 23 ON SLIDE (SCALE **C**) OPPOSITE 475

HAIR LINE

1ST FIND 475 ON SCALE **C**

20.65

FIG. 10.—Detail of **D** and **C** scales showing how to divide numbers of three figures each.

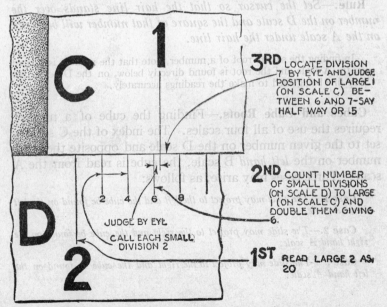

3RD LOCATE DIVISION 7 BY EYE AND JUDGE POSITION OF LARGE 1 (ON SCALE **C**) BETWEEN 6 AND 7—SAY HALF WAY OR .5

2ND COUNT NUMBER OF SMALL DIVISIONS (ON SCALE **D**) TO LARGE 1 (ON SCALE **C**) AND DOUBLE THEM GIVING 6.

JUDGE BY EYE

CALL EACH SMALL DIVISION 2

1ST READ LARGE 2 AS 20

FIG. 11.—Magnified detail of **D** and **C** scales showing how to read the answer in the example as given in fig. 10.

independently. This example illustrates how to read a number of four figures as explained under figs. 10 and 11.

Continued Multiplication.—When there are more than two factors proceed as follows:

Rule.—*Multiply the first two factors in the regular way; set hair line to register first product and continue by placing index to register with hair line.*

Squares and Square Roots.—These are found by using the A and D scales. Thus:

Rule.—*Set the cursor so that the hair line stands over the number on the D scale and the square of that number will be found on the A scale under the hair line.*

In finding the square root of a number, note that the number is located on the A scale and the root is found directly below, on the D scale, the hair line being used to make the readings accurately.

Cubes and Cube Roots.—Finding the cube of a number requires the use of all four scales. The index of the C scale is set to the given number on the D scale and opposite the same number on the *left hand* B scale, the cube is read from the A scale. Three cases may arise, as follows:

Case 1.—*The slide may project to the left and the cube be found on the left hand A scale.*

Case 2.—*The slide may project to the right and the cube be found on the right hand A scale.*

Case 3.—*The slide may project to the right and the cube be found on the left hand A scale.*

Read AUDELS MECHANICS GUIDES *for profit*

INVEST IN YOURSELF 15 MINUTES A DAY

☐ AUDELS WELDERS GUIDE · · · · · · · · · · · $1

A CONCISE, PRACTICAL TEXT ON OPERATION AND MAINTENANCE OF ALL WELDING MACHINES, FOR ALL MECHANICS.

Over 400 pages, fully illustrated, 5 x 6½ x 2, flexible covers.

Covers Electric, Oxy-acetylene, Thermit, Unionmelt Welding for sheet metal, spot and pipe welds, pressure vessels and aluminum, copper, brass, bronze and other metals, airplane work, surface hardening and hard facing, cutting, brazing—eye protection. EVERY WELDER SHOULD OWN THIS GUIDE.

☐ AUDELS ANSWERS ON BLUE PRINT READING · · · $2

COVERS ALL TYPES OF BLUE PRINT READING FOR MECHANICS AND BUILDERS.

376 pages, very fully illustrated, service bound, pocket size.

How to read scales—the standard symbols—detail and assembly prints—the different kinds of working drawings; orthographic, pictorial, descriptive—development by parallel and radial lines, conventional lines triangulation. Warped and other surfaces—specifications—how to sketch—how to make working drawings—how to make blue prints—short cuts—helps—hints and suggestions.

"The blue print of to-day is the machine of to-morrow." The man who can read blue prints is in line for a better job. This book gives you this secret language, step by step in easy stages.

NO OTHER TRADE BOOK LIKE IT—NEW, COMPLETE.

☐ AUDELS OIL BURNER GUIDE · · · · · · · · · · · · · $1

A new practical, concise treatise explaining in detail both domestic & industrial oil burners, including electrical hook ups and wiring diagrams.

Over 375 pages, 320 illustrations & diagrams. Flexible binding, pocket size.

Fully covering the Theory, Construction, Installation, Operation, Testing, Servicing & Repair of all oil burner equipment. **Fully indexed for ready reference.**

☐ Audels REFRIGERATION & Air Conditioning Guide $4

4 Books in One; covering basic principles, servicing, operation, repair of:—1. Household Refrigeration 2. Special Refrigeration Units. 3. Commercial and Industrial Refrigeration. 4. Air Conditioning Systems.

A gold mine of essential important facts for Engineers, Servicemen and Users.

A Good Book is a Good Friend! Here you have at your fingers' ends a Complete Library in ONE VOLUME, the necessary data you have been looking for on: MODERN UNITS, SYSTEMS & MACHINES, REFRIGER ANTS including Freon, Quick Freezing, Lockers, Water Coolers & Air Conditioning Systems.

1280 Pages, 46 Chapters all Fully Illustrated & Indexed for Ready Reference with Answers to Your Questions.